#JAY'S VIRTUAL Pub Quiz Book 2

By Jay Flynn

A few things about Jay…

Jay Flynn was awarded an MBE by Her Majesty Queen Elizabeth II in her 2020 birthday honours list.

A record-breaking 182,513 households played along with Jay's Virtual Pub Quiz on Thursday April 30, 2020, to set a new Guinness World Records title for most viewers of a live YouTube quiz stream.

Jay was made an England Lionheart, No. 23. A Lionheart is someone who has saved lives, inspired communities, undertaken phenomenal fundraising efforts or simply entertained others during the challenging months of lockdown. The late Captain Sir Tom Moore was the first member of the Lionhearts squad and its captain.

Jay was also ITV Pride of Britain Regional Fundraiser of the Year Finalist for 2020.

He is also the BBC Radio 2 Zoe Ball Breakfast Show official quizmaster.

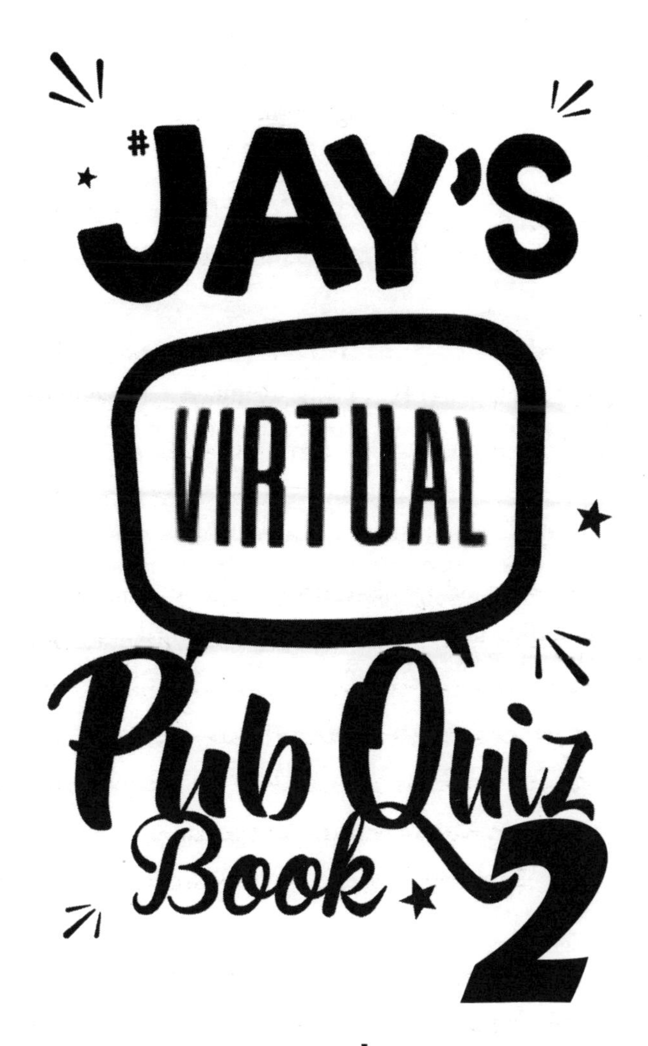

By Jay Flynn

MIRROR BOOKS

Published in Great Britain and Ireland in 2021 by
Mirror Books, a Reach PLC business.

www.mirrorbooks.co.uk

Print ISBN 9781913406776
eBook ISBN 9781913406783

Printed and bound in Great Britain by
CPI Group (UK) Ltd, Croydon, CR0 4YY

A CIP catalogue record for this book is available from the British Library.

Grandad: Book 2!
I hope you are still smiling down on me from up there.

To Jack: Keep being you every day. You are the most amazing boy we could ever have wished for.

The Geberal Nutjobs: Thank you for your continued support and faith.

Contents

Foreword page ix
Introduction page xiii
Top Tips for Hosting a Quiz page xviii

Quiz 1 – 5 page 21
Quiz 6 – 10 page 43
Quiz 11 – 15 page 67
Quiz 16 – 20 page 89
Quiz 21 – 25 page 113
Quiz 26 – 30 page 136
Specialist Rounds page 157
Readers' Round page 193

Answers page 205

Charities and Support page 307
Thank Yous page 309

Notes page 311

Foreword

During the back end of 2017, my daily ritual became sitting with Jay in a cramped little office in our car dealership, whilst we bonded over Tesco meal deals, Haribo and the occasional shared grumble for the job. If you'd have said to me back then, that in four years' time Jay would be an internet sensation, an MBE and a welcome guest in over 186,000 households, I'd have probably said: "Yeah, it's Jay, that sounds about right."

Jay and I met back in 2013. We were both dipping in and out of the motor trade for many years, working with each other about three times across the eight years I have known him. During that time I had a tendency to gatecrash Jay's Thursday evenings at his local pub quiz; as a competitive quizzer and insufferable know-it-all, I was welcomed into his team with slightly parted arms.

I remember learning at this time about Jay's years living on the streets of London. I recall thinking how could this man, the most helpful and hardworking person I know, have homelessness as his only option? As Jay explained his story to me, I found such respect and admiration for him and he helped me understand that everyone has their own story and no one on the streets deserves my judgement, only my help.

When we had both had enough of selling cars and Jay moved into the pub business, I would regularly call in on Jay in his Darwen pub, usually with a motley crew of drunken friends in tow and always to Jay's delight. Jay was a natural behind the bar, always smiling, always helpful, and certainly always willing to call you a taxi home! One of my most cherished memories of Jay in his pub, I was desperate to find a last-minute venue for my grandma's 80th birthday party. At the time my grandma was struggling with dementia and finding a venue that would be suitable was difficult. Jay didn't even bat an eyelid at closing the pub to the public, helping me find a DJ and catering, and putting me at ease throughout the entire evening. As it turned out, this was the last birthday we spent with her, so for Jay's kindness to her that evening, I will be forever grateful.

As March 2020 rolled around, I found myself – as many millennials did – back home with my parents and working from home as the country submitted to what we now know as Lockdown One. Luckily, I get my love for quizzing from my parents, so when we caught wind of this local online pub quiz, the three of us agreed to settle in on Thursday 26 March and support my old friend Jay. I think we all know what happened next…

I so clearly remember watching Jay's face on that first quiz, he was in utter awe, absolute disbelief that this many people could have tuned in to an ex-pub landlord from Darwen reading out 50 quiz questions. Lockdown brought some strange things to the country, clapping for the NHS, home-schooling, toilet roll shortages, but Jay's Virtual Pub Quiz will always be the most memorable for me.

Weeks and months passed and my parents and I continued to gather each Thursday evening. We spread the word and got more teams on board, playing against teams in France. We sat and watched as the viewers rose and the celebrities sang and the money raised for charity climbed, but Jay stayed exactly the same, humbled, grateful, just a normal person who didn't claim to be an expert, but just what the country needed and loved. I would turn on BBC News and see Jay chatting away to himself as the quiz was recommended as one of the best ways to spend lockdown.

Lockdown was then tinged with sadness for my household as we lost my grandma in June 2020. Jay once again showed his generosity and kindness by donating a large sum of money to my grandma's charity appeal, which I set up as I ran a marathon in her name. I hadn't seen the bloke in over a year and here he was still spreading the love. In his words in a text after I thanked him for the donation, he said: "As I go on this weird and crazy journey there will be people that I will lose from my life and then there are genuine people that I will always want as friends, so I'm happy to help out when I can and especially for such a great cause." I think it's important that people hear these little snippets from Jay, he is truly the most selfless and generous person I have ever met.

Jay first mentioned me joining team JVPQ when we met for a coffee in September 2020. We sat across from each other as I watched a woman pass and whisper to her partner, "That's Jay! The quiz guy," and at that point it hit me that I was joining something special. As he explained that he wanted me to be in charge of his social media platforms, I had to try hard not to fangirl a bit. It took no contemplation for me to say yes and, of course, the rest is history.

Fast forward to July 2021, it's been a crazy year for JVPQ. A book launch, an MBE, a name in Christmas lights on Oxford Street, countless private quizzes, some incredible partnerships. If readers take anything away from this, it should be the understanding that Jay works stupidly hard every day, always wanting to make his family proud and do right by his audience.

I know that I have a friend for life in Jay, but I think I've probably known that since 2013. When I tell people that this whole crazy experience hasn't changed him, I couldn't be more honest. He is still humble, insecure, generous and kind, and always has another hair-brained idea up his sleeve for me and Alex to sigh at. Thank you, Jay, I'm not sure where I (or the country) would be without you.

All my love, Bek

Introduction

Hi and welcome to Book 2! If you are new around here let me start by saying hi! My name is Jay Flynn and I am the creator, producer, director, sound engineer (sometimes if it works) and host of Jay's Virtual Pub Quiz, live every Thursday and Saturday night on YouTube and Facebook. Born in the first lockdown and still entertaining people every week around the world! A lot has happened since we last got together in book form, so let me try to bring you up to speed.

I finished the first book at the end of summer 2020. We were still in a strange place as a nation where we didn't really know what we were allowed to do for the best. But I still carried on with the live quizzes regardless. Tens of thousands of households and individuals continued to sit and laugh at my mistakes, accidental mutings and the countless incorrect or controversial answers displayed on screen. But when I was finishing off the first book, I was hiding a secret not just from our incredible community but also from some of my closest friends and family: I had received a letter from Buckingham Palace asking if I would be willing to accept an MBE for services to charity during the pandemic. Now I'm rubbish at keeping big news like that secret and it took every ounce of strength to not suddenly blurt it out one Thursday night. But I'm glad I did. The list was published at 10:30pm on 10 October, just a couple of days after the first book was released. I'm so glad I kept the secret as I first revealed the news to the Super Quizzer Patreons on a live Zoom and then a Facebook Live to the whole community. It was very emotional reading the comments from everyone and I had something in my eye that didn't help, but the reaction was so overwhelming. Without a doubt the biggest thing I had ever achieved in my life and I'm so grateful to anyone who nominated myself for the honour. The world works in mysterious ways and, only a week before, I had been inducted into the England Lionhearts squad, with the No23 alongside our dearly missed No1, Captain Sir Tom Moore. That was a massive surprise to me as Alex – my right-hand man, confidant, guidance counsellor and friend – had arranged all the details and kept them secret from me, and even involved my wife Sarah and my mother-in-law Gill in the whole ruse. So in the space of a couple of weeks I had my first ever book out, been made an England Lionheart and accepted an MBE. Suffice to say one of those on their own would have been an incredible moment.

There was another award to follow as The Book of Man made me one of their Men of the Year for 2020 and sent an awesome award to go with it. This past year-and-a-half has gone by in such a blur it's been amazing, emotional, draining and so much fun all in one!

On top of all of that I have managed to do two in-person quizzes, one at the Great British Drive In in the wonderful Staforshire (that's a deliberate spelling mistake, you had to be there!). I also did one here in Darwen as well to more than 100 people and it was incredible standing on those stages and seeing everyone and how much fun they were having. I'm still live every Thursday morning on Zoe Ball's Breakfast Show, quizzing the team with five questions. It's worth waking up really early just to hear the insane answers of Richie Anderson, who I was honoured to be joined by in hosting the quiz live on a Thursday night in aid of Samaritans. On that note I have had the honour of talking to some truly A-List stars this past year, whilst putting together some specialist quizzes for charities. Billie Piper and Matt Smith for a Doctor Who quiz and Nathalie Emmanuel and Jacob Anderson for a very special Game of Thrones quiz (both quizzes are still available on the channel and well worth a watch). Hugh Dennis and Ed Byrne are among so many others who have given up their time to be a part of the quizzes and raise so much money for charities up and down the country. It is, however, because of your support that we have raised over £1million for them.

By the time you have this book in your hands I will have run the London Marathon in aid of The Connection, the homeless charity that supported me and got me off the streets and back to normality. There is a very sentimental reason behind this as I'll be running past my bench: Number 3, Riverside View, Victoria Embankment. Never all those years ago did I think I would ever be running past it having achieved so much.

People keep asking me why am I still doing it, everything's getting back to normal. Well for that I need to take you back further than all of this. As most of you will know I was homeless on the streets of London for two years at the end of the Noughties. I had absolutely nothing and no one. I was alone and isolated, I didn't have people to talk to every day. I didn't have a routine or things to look forward to. I was just me, myself and I. And it was tough. So when the pandemic hit and everyone was forced into staying home, it reminded me of those times. And then people getting in touch who lived on their own and using the quiz to re-connect with family or friends, or to just be a familiar presence in their homes twice a week, made me realise, that although my quiz was born out of a mistake on social media in some of the darkest times in the history of the world, it still could serve a purpose and have a place in this new world.

Even now I speak to people who tell me stories of how they have bonded with new flatmates, or re-connected with family and friends all over the world, or just to say that hearing my voice coming from the TV, they know what day of the week it is. So it's great being recognised by Her Majesty and the Prime Minister, but the feedback, messages and support from the incredible 500k-strong community that we have and how I have helped in just a small way, means the absolute world to me. I always joked that I would continue until there is only one person watching, which would probably be my mum. Well, I now know there will be thousands still watching, and I will be there for you as well.

Thanks for reading, let us know your scores across all our social media.

Take care and as always from me,

Stay safe.

Jay

P.S. Geberal Knowledge is our version of General Knowledge, it's been there since day one and it's what we call it around here. Just one of a number of slips that include Tome Cruise, Jamie Dodger and the complete relocation of Milton Keynes!

Hosting a quiz. Top Tips!

For consistency this is repeated from the last book as it's good advice, just slightly tweaked.

The hardest part of running any quiz is the questions! Researching and writing questions is the part that takes the longest and no matter how many times you check the answers, mistakes will always occur! Actually hosting a quiz is a piece of cake, so to help you make your quiz night go as smooth as possible, here are my top tips to get you going.

Get the right format. On the live quizzes I settled into a format of 50 questions spilt over five rounds. It allowed for the perfect balance of categories and difficulty level, without being too short or too long. But every quiz night could be different. The book is laid out in the live quiz format of 50 question quizzes, but you might want to have 100 questions or maybe less than 50. As the host, you decide! This time around I have included some specialist quizzes and also some children-specific quizzes as well.

Know your audience! The next tip is to make sure that you know your audience. There is no point turning up with 50 questions on sport if your audience don't know their Andy Murrays from their Lewis Hamiltons! Tailor your quiz to your audience to keep them engaged.

Prepare! Once you have your format and know your audience, read through your questions. Check your answers, be comfortable with word pronunciations. For the quiz itself, make sure you have pens and paper.

Confidence! When hosting the actual quiz, have confidence. Deliver each one as you believe in it and don't fear the banter that will come back to you. Make jokes and put everyone at ease, but as the quizmaster, keep control!

Be the ringmaster! As the host, you are the ringmaster, you are in charge. The quizmaster is always right! Even if they are blue in the face that they are right, your decision is final!

Have fun! There is a sense of great feeling that when you get to that final answer, seeing the winning team celebrate, but the losing teams' determination to win next time makes it worthwhile!

Hosting a quiz, playing a quiz, or just reading the questions in the book for fun, it adds to our knowledge. You might not necessarily know the answer to every question, otherwise you'd be a genius with an IQ over 200! But that new random fact you've learnt might just help in the future!

Quiz 1

ROUND 1: TV

1. Who played Dot Cotton in EastEnders?
2. Which American medical drama series starred George Clooney, Noah Wyle and Alex Kingston?
3. Sean Bean played which character in Game Of Thrones?
4. In which TV series would you find the Sacred Heart Hospital?
5. Ringo Starr was the original narrator for which children's TV series?
6. Which of these is the odd one out? Phone A Friend, Ask The Audience, Phone A Friend and Pass.
7. What was Fonzie's real name in Happy Days?
8. Who was captain of the of the ship "The Black Pig"?
9. Which weatherman failed to warn people about the big storm of 1987?
10. The Sunshine Cab Company could be found in which TV show?

ROUND 2: SCIENCE

1. Which is the largest planet in the solar system?
2. How many sides does a trapezium or trapezoid have?
3. What name is given to a subatomic particle carrying a negative charge?
4. Which metal is extracted from bauxite ore?
5. What is the medical name for short-sightedness?
6. What element has the chemical symbol W?
7. If you divide mass by volume, what do you get?
8. Iron pyrite is better known by which nickname?
9. In computing terms, what does VoIP stand for?
10. How is hydrated magnesium sulphate better known?

ROUND 3: SPORT

1. In which year was Maradona's Hand Of God?
2. What type of tower is on the badge of the football club Paris Saint-Germain?
3. In which country would you find the Circuit de Catalunya?

4. In bowls, what is the target ball called?
5. What number shirt does a Rugby Union scrum-half usually wear?
6. What does DRS stand for in Formula 1?
7. With which sport would you associate Mickey Mantle?
8. What is the distance from the floor to the basketball hoop?
9. The winners of the Europa League and Champions league meet in which annual tournament?
10. How many points are scored for a field goal in American Football?

ROUND 4: PEOPLE

1. Which actress was married eight times and had husbands including Richard Burton and Conrad Hilton Junior?
2. The Hunchback of Notre Dame was known by what other name?
3. Who was born Lawrence Harvey Zeiger?
4. Scientist Galileo Galilei was which nationality?

5. What was Elvis Presley's middle name?
6. Who was born Margaret Hilda Roberts?
7. Bernie Taupin is a famous lyricist who had most of his success with whom?
8. How was Samuel Langhorne Clemens better known?
9. Who was Warren Beatty's famous sister?
10. Timothy Laurence is the husband of which Royal Family member?

ROUND 5: GEBERAL KNOWLEDGE

1. Aslan is a lion in which children's book and TV series?
2. In which game might you castle?
3. Which composer wrote Godspell, Pippin and Wicked?
4. Who wrote the poem, I Wandered Lonely As A Cloud?
5. What does the 'E' stand for in e-mail?
6. Who is Queen Elizabeth's second eldest child?
7. Shuffle, Classic and Touch are variations of what?

8. What is longer in distance, one furlong or one mile?
9. In the binary system, what is the largest number?
10. A ream of paper is how many sheets in total?

Quiz 2

ROUND 1: FILM

1. Who directed Jaws?
2. What was the name of Rose's fiancé in Titanic?
3. The first rule is you don't talk about it. Which film?
4. Which US president had a cameo in Home Alone 2: Lost In New York?
5. What is the name of the elderly gold prospector in the film Toy Story 2?
6. Baby Driver, starring Ansel Elgort, Lily James and Kevin Spacey, was directed by whom?
7. An all-star cast including, Chris Pratt, Will Arnett,

Cobie Smulders, Morgan Freeman and Liam Neeson, voice characters in which 2014 movie?

8. Starring Tommy Lee Jones and Don Cheadle, name the 1997 disaster movie set in Los Angeles?
9. Complete the title of the Eighties British film: Rita, Sue And....?
10. Who played Edna Turnblad in the 2007 movie version of Hairspray?

ROUND 2: NATURE

1. How many hearts does an octopus have?
2. Are worker ants male or female?
3. What is the collective name for a group of frogs?
4. In which organ of the human body would you find the alveoli?
5. How many pairs of chromosomes make up the DNA of a normal human body?
6. Which Spanish word translates as "little fly"?
7. For a soil to be described as permafrost, what temperature does it need to remain below for two years?

8. An anemometer measures what?
9. What is the medical name for the lower jawbone?
10. Which has more teeth: reptiles or mammals?

zoom 19/12/21

ROUND 3: ART AND LITERATURE

1. Who wrote Doctor Zhivago?
2. In which book would you find the character Phileas Fogg?
3. Who wrote the book Gone With The Wind?
4. Which art gallery would you find at Trafalgar Square in London?
5. Whose first published novel was The Hunt For Red October in 1984?
6. What is the name of Washington Irving's 1819 short story about a man who sleeps for 20 years?
7. Which little girl was found inside the petals of a flower in the fairy tale?
8. What was the name of Snoopy's closest non-human friend?
9. What was the name of the Inspector created by Ruth Rendell?

10. Who wrote the Hunchback of Notre Dame?

ROUND 4: GEOGRAPHY

family zoom 2/1/22

1. Which city is spread over two continents?
2. What is the oldest active volcano on the planet?
3. In which US state would you find Fort Knox?
4. What is the biggest city in Africa by population?
5. What is the second largest city in Australia?
6. What is the currency of Sweden?
7. In which US state is Niagara Falls?
8. What is the currency of Mexico?
9. Which sea separates the Italian and Balkan peninsulas?
10. What body of water separates the two main islands of New Zealand?

ROUND 5: GEBERAL KNOWLEDGE

fam zoom 9/1/22

1. Who is Peter Pan's enemy?
2. What does Norway give to Britain every year around Christmas time?

3. Which star sign comes last alphabetically?
4. What is the only mainland South American nation whose official language is English?
5. How many bronze lions would you find in Trafalgar Square in London?
6. What material can be measured in reams?
7. On a UK Monopoly board, which space follows Mayfair?
8. What does the M stand for in GMT?
9. In which month is St Andrew's Day?
10. What does the surname Singh mean when translated into English?

Quiz 3

ROUND 1: MUSIC

1. Whose first UK number-one single was All Shook Up in 1957?
2. Complete the name of the American hard rock band: Grand Funk... ?
3. Which member of the Jackson family hit number two with The Best Things In Life Are Free.
4. Who had Nineties hits with Thank You and Ironic?
5. The Everly Brothers had a hit with Wake Up Little whom?
6. Livin' La Vida Loca was a 1999 hit for which artist?
7. How many James Bond theme tunes did Shirley Bassey sing?
8. Which musician had the nickname Slowhand?
9. What did Ronan Keating say Life was?
10. Madison Avenue didn't want you to call them what, according to the title of their Noughties song?

ROUND 2: FOOD AND DRINK

1. How many standard 750ml bottles of wine would fit into a Methuselah?
2. What is the head waiter or host at a French restaurant called?
3. “The red car and the blue car had a race, all that red could do was stuff his face” are lines from which chocolate bar advert?
4. Pineapples – do they grow on trees or on the ground?
5. Focaccia bread originated in which country?
6. What alcohol forms the base for Drambuie?
7. What flavour is the traditional Greek aperitif Ouzo?
8. Crudites is a French word for raw what?
9. What is a key ingredient of a Dahl recipe?
10. What is the main alcoholic component of a Daiquiri?

ROUND 3: HISTORY

1. How many years was the Hundred Years War on for?

2. In which historic castle are the Crown Jewels kept?
3. How many British monarchs have celebrated Diamond Jubilees?
4. What name was given to the World War Two B-17 bomber?
5. What was the name of the ship that brought the first Pilgrims to the US in 1620?
6. Who was responsible for the Barings Bank collapse in 1995?
7. What was Apollo 11's lunar module called?
8. Who was Sandra Rivett's employer and suspected murderer?
9. Robert the Bruce was crowned King of where in 1306?
10. Who was married to Marie Antoinette and the last King of Scotland?

ROUND 4: SCIENCE

1. What has a higher pH level, acids or alkaline?
2. 1,000 gigabytes is equivalent to one what?
3. Which country lended its name to a flu pandemic

during the early 20th century?

4. Rickets is a deficiency of which vitamin?
5. In computing, what does the M stand for in CMYK?
6. What is the medical term for the white part of the eye?
7. Who is credited with discovering penicillin in 1928?
8. Hypoxia is the starvation of what?
9. A group of Beavers is known as a family and a what?
10. A sphygmomanometer measures what?

ROUND 5: GEBERAL KNOWLEDGE

1. What came first: PlayerUnknown's Battlegrounds or Fortnite?
2. In which country was Julian Assange born?
3. What is Prince William's second name?
4. Which instant camera was first sold in 1948?
5. 'Steven Frayne' is the real name of which very popular British entertainer?
6. On a standard computer keyboard, what key is above the Enter key?

7. What is the best hand in a game of Poker?
8. The three Olympic class liners were Titanic, Britannic and which other?
9. Who created the cartoon Garfield?
10. What was Cinderella's lost slipper made of?

Quiz 4

ROUND 1: TV

1. The Warblers were a fictional a capella group in which American TV series?
2. Helen Hayes, Joan Hickson, Geraldine McEwan and Julia McKenzie have all played which character on TV?
3. Which TV sitcom was set in Whitbury New Town Leisure Centre?
4. Adam West played which superhero?

5. The second round of which kids Nineties TV show was the Fun Kart Grand Prix?
6. Mork from Mork and Mindy first appeared in which TV show?
7. Who was known as "The Crocodile Hunter"?
8. Which animated characters lived at 62 West Wallaby Street?
9. Whose alter ego is the Pub Landlord?
10. Who is Bob The Builder's business partner?

ROUND 2: SPORT

1. In which country where the first Olympic Games held?
2. Which lawn sport, French in name, has only ever made one appearance at the Olympic Games?
3. In football, what does the A stand for in VAR?
4. What is Tiger Woods' first name?
5. What is the length in feet of a standard bowling alley?
6. How far from the goal line should the penalty spot be in an 11-a-side football match?

7. Shooting and skiing combine to make which sport?
8. What is the diameter in inches of a dart board?
9. How many ways can you be declared 'out' in cricket?
10. The British & Irish Lions compete in which sport?

ROUND 3: PEOPLE

6/3/22 Emily zoom

1. What was the name of the young girl who wrote a diary whilst in hiding during World War Two?
2. Who was known as Hanoi Jane?
3. Tim Cook replaced whom as Apple CEO?
4. Who killed Lee Harvey Oswald?
5. How is Robert Zimmerman better known?
6. Which former MP dated weather reporter Sian Lloyd?
7. The Fat Duck restaurant in Bray, Berkshire, was the brainchild of which TV chef?
8. Florence Nightingale was born in which country?
9. Who was convicted as the Unabomber?
10. Who was the main creator and current CEO of Facebook?

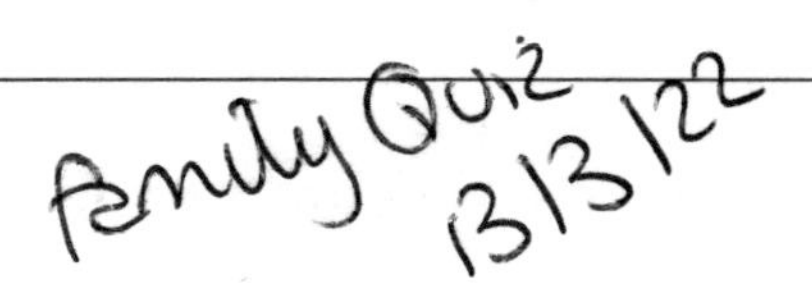

ROUND 4: PLACES

1. Which county in the UK is known as the Red Rose county?
2. In which country is the Tanami Desert?
3. At which ski resort would you find the Cresta Run?
4. St. Agnes, St. Helen's, St. Martin's and St. Mary's islands are collectively known as what?
5. What is Brazil's largest city by population?
6. What became the Kennedy Space Centre?
7. What is the largest desert region in Asia?
8. Which country was expelled from Malaysia in 1965?
9. What is the highest mountain in Jamaica called?
10. In which Indian city would you find the Taj Mahal?

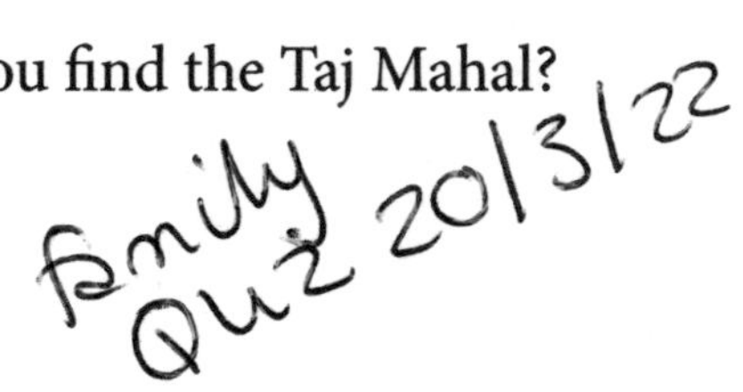

ROUND 5: GEBERAL KNOWLEDGE

1. Michael, Trevor and Franklin are the lead characters in which 2013 game?
2. In which country was Boris Johnson born?
3. The Pulitzer Prize is awarded by which university?

4. The world's largest power station is a dam in China. True or false?
5. What was the name of the doomed 1960s stereo cartridge system?
6. EA Sports has been making which football game for decades?
7. What is the lowest-scoring tile in a game of Scrabble?
8. Who owned the cartoon dog Gnasher?
9. Inverted, suspended, corkscrew and vertical drop are all types of what?
10. The Suez Canal connects the Red Sea to which other water body?

Quiz 5

ROUND 1: FILM

1. What was the character name of the young boy in ET?
2. Ryan Gosling and Rachel McAdams play Noah and Allison in which romantic film?
3. Who played Wordsworth the butler in the classic film Clue?
4. What is the name of the car in Grease?
5. In which movie franchise would you find the Mos Eisley Cantina?
6. Will Smith, Robert De Niro and Renee Zellweger among others voiced characters in which 2004 film?
7. In which year was Silence Of The Lambs released?
8. Who did Gene Wilder play in the original version of Charlie And The Chocolate Factory?
9. What is Dorothy's surname in the Wizard Of Oz?
10. What are the first names of the Blues Brothers characters?

ROUND 2: NATURE

1. What is the name for a female ferret that hasn't been spayed?
2. What is a female alligator called?
3. What is a group of lions called?
4. What is another name for the thigh bone?
5. Cerumen is a bodily secretion better known by which name?
6. Narcolepsy is what kind of disorder?
7. Gorham's disease affects which part of the body?
8. What is the most common term for a group of grasshoppers?
9. A baby ferret is called what?
10. Cynophobia is a fear of which animal?

ROUND 3: ART AND LITERATURE

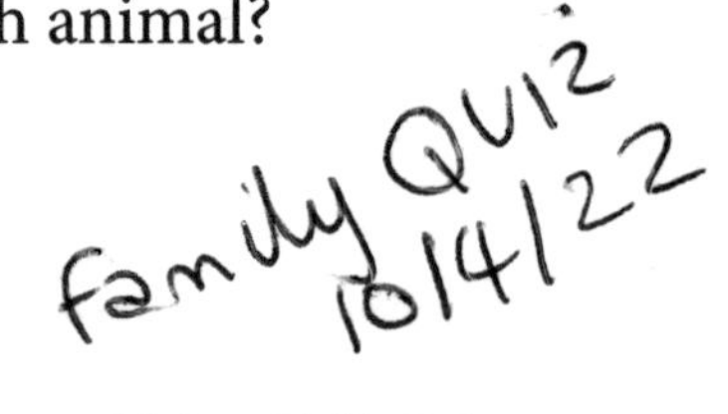

1. The Two Towers, The Hobbit and The Fall Of Gondolin were all books by which author?
2. Leonardo Da Vinci painted The Last what?
3. What is the last book of the Old Testament?

4. Who was the sculptor behind the Angel of the North?
5. Who wrote War Of The Worlds?
6. How many people are depicted in The Last Supper?
7. In which novel would you find the opening line, "Call me Ishmael"?
8. What was Miss Marple's first name?
9. Who wrote a Tale Of Two Cities?
10. Who wrote The Godfather?

ROUND 4: GEOGRAPHY

1. Which Spanish island saw the worst aviation disaster in history?
2. What does the DC stand for in Washington DC?
3. Which modern-day Indian city used to be called Madras?
4. What is the second largest continent by area?
5. What is the largest lake in Africa?
6. Which island country's national language is Malagasy?

7. Which country sits between Norway and Finland?
8. Cape Verde is an island just to the west of which continent?
9. How many red stripes are on the flag of the USA?
10. Which island gained independence from the UK in 1960?

ROUND 5: GEBERAL KNOWLEDGE

1. Which classic Nintendo game made the switch to a mobile augmented reality game in 2016?
2. Evita, Cats and Jesus Christ Superstar were musicals written by which composer?
3. Which country was allowed to participate on Eurovision in 2015, despite not being a European country?
4. Which is the furthest of the eight planets from the sun?
5. Which rock star was born Farrokh Bulsara in 1946?
6. What is the end to this line, "One, two, buckle my shoe, three, four..."?
7. In which game did Super Mario make his first appearance?

8. Which metal object was traditionally found on the back of cowboy boots?
9. Timmy was the name of the dog in which cartoon series?
10. Calligraphy is the art of doing what artistically?

Quiz 6

ROUND 1: MUSIC

1. What was the name of Cliff Richard's backing band between 1958-1968?
2. Billy Gibbons is the front man for which American rock band?
3. Who was George Michael's partner in Wham?
4. Richard Ashcroft was the frontman for which Nineties group?
5. Who had a 1960 hit with their cover version of the song At Last?

6. According to the 1964 Beatles classic, how many days a week were there?
7. All the members of ABBA were born in Sweden. True or false?
8. Who was born Marvin Lee Aday?
9. What is Paul McCartney's middle name?
10. Yazoo was made up of Vince Clarke and which female singer?

ROUND 2: SCIENCE

1. Photosynthesis occurs in which part of a plant?
2. In which part of the car would you find sulphuric acid?
3. What is the chemical name for the formula CH4?
4. What does a rhinologist study?
5. What nationality was Alfred Nobel?
6. Which planet do Phobos and Deimos belong to?
7. Vitamin A improves humans' ability to see where?
8. A gigawatt is a billion what?

9. What does PVC stand for?
10. What does the B stand for in USB?

ROUND 3: FOOD AND DRINK

1. What came first in the UK, McDonald's or Burger King?
2. Which punch drink, originating in Spain and Portugal, has the base of red wine and is served with chunks of fruit?
3. In which restaurant would you find the following types of chicken: lemon and herb, mango and lime, and peri-peri?
4. Croutons are small, toasted pieces of what?
5. Battenberg cake is covered in what?
6. Douwe Egberts is a brand of which drink?
7. What is the biggest component of a Rocky Road?
8. A dish known as Florentine is cooked with what?
9. Burgundy is a wine region in which country?
10. Which country does Singha beer originate?

ROUND 4: HISTORY

1. In which year did the Battle of Waterloo take place?
2. A bakery is said to be the site that caused which major disaster in 1666?
3. Who led the Roman invasion of Britain in 55BC?
4. What was the name of the volcano that destroyed Pompeii?
5. Which age came straight before the Iron Age?
6. Which country is the site of the ancient city of Troy?
7. The French Revolution started with the storming of where?
8. James Cook named Tonga the what Islands?
9. Who was said to be raised by wolves and the mythical twin founders of Rome?
10. William Booth founded which organisation in 1865?

ROUND 5: GEBERAL KNOWLEDGE

1. Aiden Pearce was a hacker in which game?
2. What is the highest number used in standard sudoku?
3. Which newspaper came first in the UK, the Daily Mirror or Daily Mail?
4. The fictional characters Dr Henry and Mr Edward are better known by which names?
5. In the Charles Dickens novel Oliver Twist, how did Fagin die?
6. What was the name of Betty and Barney's child in the Flintstones?
7. How many checkers does each player start a game of Backgammon with?
8. Routemaster was a type of what?
9. What do all of the internal angles of a square add up to?
10. What might a bibliophile collect?

Quiz 7

ROUND 1: TV

1. What was the name of Channel 5's attempt at a British soap opera?
2. Which comedy, starring Penelope Keith and Felicity Kendal, ran for three years between 1975 and 1978?
3. Gizmo was a cute and cuddly creature in which Eighties movie?
4. "Goodbye grey sky, hello blue, there's nothing can hold me when I hold you" is a line from which Seventies/Eighties TV show theme tune?
5. Who played Wonder Woman in the Seventies TV show of the same name?
6. Complete the name of the political drama: House Of...?
7. Kiefer Sutherland played the president in which Netflix original series?
8. Who played the travelling TV repairman in Goodnight Sweetheart?

9. What was the name of Channel 4's breakfast show, presented by Johnny Vaughan?

10. What was Mr Benn's address?

ROUND 2: FOOD AND DRINK

1. What is added to a martini, to make it a Dirty Martini?

2. Which manufacturer makes the Wispa and Wispa Gold chocolate bars?

3. Chocolate shortbread and what other ingredient make up millionaire shortbread?

4. What was the favourite food of the Teenage Mutant Ninja Turtles?

5. Profiterole uses what type of pastry?

6. What spirit is traditionally added to butter and served alongside Christmas pudding?

7. Angels on Horseback are oysters wrapped in what?

8. In which country would you traditionally find pecan pie?

9. What is the Scottish version of a crumpet called?

10. Which lager had the slogan "Refreshes the parts other beers can't reach"?

ROUND 3: ART AND LITERATURE

1. Who wrote the autobiography entitled Long Walk To Freedom?
2. In the book Charlotte's Web, what was Charlotte?
3. Ian Fleming created which secret agent?
4. Who created the character Noddy?
5. Who wrote the Chronicles Of Narnia?
6. According to Shakespeare, what is the food of love?
7. Mozart composed The Marriage Of whom?
8. Who wrote The Jungle Book?
9. What are elephants called in the Winnie The Pooh series of books?
10. On which buildings ceiling would you find Nine Scenes From The Book Of Genesis?

ROUND 4: PEOPLE

1. Which famous musician was born in Liverpool on 9 October 1940?
2. Who was known as the Maid of Orleans?

3. John Noakes was the longest-serving presenter of which TV series?
4. Jessica Ellen Cornish is better known by which stage name?
5. Which comedian was born in Bolton and holds the Guinness World Record for the most successful stand-up tour?
6. Which retired ballerina was a judge on Strictly Come Dancing?
7. What was the surname of fashion designer Vivienne?
8. Which Olympic gymnast won back-to-back silver medals at the Olympics and went on to win Strictly Come Dancing?
9. Which former Monty Python member is well known for his travels around the world?
10. Who is the host of Would I Lie to You?

ROUND 5: GEBERAL KNOWLEDGE

1. How many suits are in a game of Mahjong?
2. Where in the world would you expect to find a car with the vehicle registration code V?

3. What is the name of the red vacuum cleaner with a face on?
4. The noble experiment of prohibition in the USA saw the ban of what?
5. What is the name of the long-running soap on Radio 4?
6. What does a Wainwright make?
7. On which surface might you find a Zamboni?
8. How many ounces to a pound?
9. In which part of your body might you get quinsy?
10. The song Memories comes from which musical?

Quiz 8

ROUND 1: FILM

1. John McClane is the main character in which movie franchise?

2. Kellerman's is a holiday resort in which film?
3. "He's not the messiah, he is a very naughty boy" is from which film?
4. Spider-Pig appeared in which TV show's jump to the big screen?
5. What colour is Dory in Finding Nemo?
6. What 2008 film tells the story of a small waste collection robot left on an abandoned Earth?
7. Name the now cult classic satirical war film that starred Neil Patrick Harris and Denise Richards.
8. Name one of the Naked Gun sequels?
9. Who did Anne Bancroft play in The Graduate?
10. Tom Hanks played on a giant floor piano in which film?

ROUND 2: SCIENCE

1. What is toxicology the study of?
2. At which value do Fahrenheit and centigrade meet?
3. Which of these is the weakest force of nature: Gravity or electromagnetic force?
4. Which chemical element has the symbol B?

5. In which part of the body would you find the tarsal bones?
6. The equinox is when the sun's direct rays cross the celestial what?
7. What was the name of the first super-continent?
8. The Earth has three layers, the crust, the mantle and...?
9. Which planet is the hottest in the solar system?
10. How many elements are there in the periodic table?

ROUND 3: SPORT

1. How many players are on a volleyball team?
2. What is the name of a golfer's assistant who carries the clubs?
3. Which country will host the 2022 World Cup finals?
4. Which colour flag indicates a faster car is about to approach in motorsport?
5. TaylorMade is a well-known name in which sport?
6. David Beckham retired from professional football playing for which club?

7. In which sport would you find the Kansas City Chiefs and Tampa Bay Buccaneers?
8. Where was Mark Cavendish born?
9. Which cricketer was known as The Cat?
10. Bob and Mike Bryan were successful sportsmen in which sport?

ROUND 4: GEOGRAPHY

1. Hollywood is in which state?
2. Havana is the capital of which country?
3. PEK is the code for which international airport?
4. What is the only sea on Earth with no coastline?
5. What country lies directly east of Haiti on the island of Hispaniola?
6. Which country has the most natural lakes?
7. What is the capital of Serbia?
8. What is the national flower of the Netherlands?
9. Which country do the Azores belong to?
10. The River Jordan flows into which Sea?

ROUND 5: GEBERAL KNOWLEDGE

1. Which former actor became governor of California in 2003?
2. The logo for which popular app consists of a white telephone in a white speech bubble on a green background?
3. How many men did the Grand Old Duke of York have?
4. What brand of toilet paper features puppies in its TV commercials?
5. Which cartoon bird's favourite song is Camptown Races?
6. In which game do you have to act out the answer without speaking?
7. Which character always carries a blanket in the cartoon strip Peanuts?
8. What is the Spanish for the number one?
9. Triskaidekaphobia is a fear of what?
10. What colour are the benches in the House of Commons?

Quiz 9

ROUND 1: MUSIC

1. Bill Medley and Bucky Heard are a musical duo originally known by which name?
2. How is Declan Patrick McManus better known?
3. David Byrne, Chris Frantz, Tina Weymouth and Jerry Harrison made up which rock band?
4. What was the British electronic group, best known for the single Set You Free, called?
5. Which singer was born Mary Isobel Catherine Bernadette O'Brien?
6. What are fans of Barry Manilow known as?
7. Who hand a long-running number one single with Love Is All Around?
8. How To Save A Life was a Noughties hit for whom?
9. Frankie Goes To Hollywood had a hit with how many tribes?
10. Who had a hit with The Final Countdown in the Eighties?

ROUND 2: NATURE

1. Which stone are the White Cliffs of Dover made out of?
2. A penguin can fly. True or false?
3. Which animal is known for its ability to roll up into a ball?
4. How many times a year does the winter solstice occur?
5. Which of these has a U-shaped snout: Alligator or crocodile?
6. Puma and lynx belong to which animal family?
7. A dog's skeleton is made up of around 319 bones. True or false?
8. What part of a shark do they use to breathe?
9. What is the top speed of the honey bee: 3.2 km/h, 32 km/h or 132 km/h?
10. Owls' eyes can't turn in their socket. True or false?

ROUND 3: HISTORY

1. Anne Boleyn was one, but who was the other wife Henry VIII had executed?

2. What broadcast did approximately 650 million people worldwide watch on 20 July 1969?
3. What English king signed the Magna Carta at Runnymede, near Windsor, on 15 June 1215?
4. James VI succeeded Elizabeth I to become King of Scots and where?
5. Operation Sea Lion was Germany's plan to invade which country in 1940?
6. Whose tomb did Edward Carter discover in 1922?
7. What name was given to the German decoding machines during World War Two?
8. Who was known as the Nine Days' Queen?
9. Which treaty formally established the European Union?
10. How many British monarchs were there during the 20th century?

ROUND 4: PLACES

1. Blenheim Palace is in which UK county?
2. North and South Korea share the same name for which currency?

3. What is the Welsh name for Wales?
4. Who did Algeria gain independence from?
5. What prehistoric monument would you find in Wiltshire?
6. Which year did Hong Kong transfer from the UK to China?
7. In which Italian city would you find the Leaning Tower?
8. What is the largest city in Pakistan by population?
9. Where would you find the Burj Khalifa?
10. What separates Alaska from Russia?

ROUND 5: GEBERAL KNOWLEDGE

1. According to the rhyme, Round And Round The Garden, like a what?
2. Moonshine was a slang term for what kind of beverage?
3. Featuring black question cards and white answer cards, what game is described at bringing out the worst in people?
4. Anne Frank was born in which European country?

5. What is the maximum number of spots on one tile in a standard set of dominoes?
6. What is the name of the puppet created by Geppetto?
7. "With great praise" is translated to which well-known phrase in Latin?
8. A word reading the same forwards and backwards is known by what name?
9. Who directed the London 2012 Olympic Games opening ceremony?
10. Name the furniture retailer famous for flat-pack furniture, Daim bars and meatballs.

Quiz 10

ROUND 1: TV

1. Which anniversary did Coronation Street celebrate with a tram crash?
2. Complete the name of this Seventies sitcom: What Ever Happened To...?
3. The character Mercedes McQueen appears in which popular UK soap?
4. Who replaced Christopher Ecclestone on Doctor Who?
5. Which Channel 4 soap opera started in 1995 and still runs today?
6. Which police show was set at Hill Street Station?
7. Which cartoon had a bar named Moe's?
8. Which character in the TV show Friends was a palaeontologist?
9. Which long-running documentary series looks at air disasters?
10. What was Lady Penelope's surname in Thunderbirds?

ROUND 2: FOOD AND DRINK

1. If you were served aloo at an Indian restaurant or takeaway, which vegetable would you be eating?
2. "Once you pop you can't stop" is the slogan to which crisp brand?
3. Horse radish is traditionally served with which roast meat?
4. What ingredient in bread causes it to rise?
5. What cheese is traditionally found on pizzas?
6. Bergamot gives which type of tea its distinctive flavour?
7. According to the advertising slogan, Australians wouldn't give a what XXXX for anything else?
8. What lager was described as reassuringly expensive?
9. Which comedian had Jimmy Con Carne crisps named after him for Comic Relief?
10. What part of an egg is also known as the Vitellus?

ROUND 3: PEOPLE

1. On which island was the Duke of Edinburgh born – Corfu or Crete?

2. Who was assassinated at the Ford's Theatre in 1865?
3. Rory Graham is better known by which stage name?
4. Kim Jong-un is believed to have studied as a child in which country?
5. Which US president lent his name to teddy bears?
6. In which country was Pablo Picasso born?
7. Who wrote The General Theory of Relativity?
8. Which singer married Lisa Marie Presley in 1994?
9. Who led the non-violent campaign for India's independence?
10. Who was the leader of the Soviet Union during World War Two?

ROUND 4: SPORT

1. In which sport do players sweep the ice?
2. The US Masters golf tournament lasts for how many days?
3. What colour is the outer bull on a standard dartboard?
4. What is the name of the ball-tracking system used in tennis?

5. How many players are on a team on the field in a game of Australian Rules Football?
6. Which nationality is F1 driver Max Verstappen?
7. The Toronto Blue Jays are the only team to win which American-based series from outside the US?
8. In which sport might you be awarded the Lonsdale Belt?
9. A shot replayed from the same position without penalty in golf is known as a what?
10. Show jumping, fencing and pistol shooting are all events in which sport?

ROUND 5: GEBERAL KNOWLEDGE

1. Which pub name links the TV series Minder and the film Shaun Of The Dead?
2. Who was the last UK act to win Eurovision?
3. Karaoke is a Japanese word that translates to what?
4. How many right angles are there in a square?
5. What word for a powerful businessman means "great prince" in Japanese?
6. 'Flossing', 'take the L' and 'fresh' are dances in which video game?

7. Which letter is yellow in the Google logo?
8. The stern is at what part of the ship?
9. Which British coin was introduced into general circulation in 1998?
10. Which animal was the mascot for Toys 'R' Us?

Quiz 11

ROUND 1: FILM

1. Who played John Hammond in Jurassic Park?
2. Shopgirl and NY152 were the online usernames in which 1998 film?
3. Elizabeth Berkley played an exotic dancer in which 1995 film?
4. Dominic Toretto is the lead character in which movie franchise?
5. What song does the main character wake up to every day in Groundhog Day?
6. Bigger, Longer & Uncut is the subtitle to which animated movie?
7. How many Oscars did Titanic win?
8. Nicole Kidman played Satine in which 2001 musical?
9. Who sung the theme tune to the 1997 James Bond film Tomorrow Never Dies?
10. Complete the 2004 Jim Carrey movie: Eternal Sunshine Of The...?

ROUND 2: SCIENCE

1. What does MRI stand for in medicine?
2. What is the scientific name for ammonia?
3. Which planet comes fourth alphabetically?
4. Gene Cernan is the last man to walk where?
5. What is the correct name for the thumb?
6. What element has the chemical symbol Ag?
7. What are the following better known as: Helium, neon and argon?
8. The bending of light from one source to another is known as what?
9. What does the L stand for in LED?
10. What was the name of NASA's last-ever shuttle mission?

ROUND 3: ART AND LITERATURE

1. Which comedian wrote the autobiography entitled The Sound Of Laughter?
2. Which street artist is responsible for the following works: One Nation Under CCTV, Balloon Girl and Dismaland?

3. Who wrote the poems If and Mandalay?
4. What does an etymologist study?
5. Which long-haired princess was locked in a tower by a witch?
6. How many black keys are on a standard 88-key piano?
7. Which famous comedian and actress wrote the autobiography Dear Fatty?
8. Which UK Prime Minister has been awarded the Nobel Prize for Literature?
9. Duncan, Donalbain and Banquo were characters in which Shakespeare play?
10. Which author was born Charles Lutwidge Dodgson?

ROUND 4: GEOGRAPHY

1. Which state is known as the gambling and entertainment capital of the USA?
2. Which lake is the world's largest?
3. In what country is Athens the capital city?
4. What is the tallest building in the UK?
5. Lake Tahoe borders which two US states?

6. What country, slightly larger than Texas, uses the "kwacha" as its currency?
7. Which sea does Azerbaijan sit on?
8. Red and what other colour make up the flag of Poland?
9. The Mekong Delta flows into which sea?
10. Cathay Pacific is the flag carrier for where?

ROUND 5: GEBERAL KNOWLEDGE

1. Who is Mario's brother in the video games?
2. What does the P stand for in RSVP?
3. Who delivered the Gettysburg Address?
4. Percy Shaw invented which road safety device?
5. How many sides does a dodecagon have?
6. How many boys' names are featured in the phonetic alphabet?
7. Which pop star was the focus of the 1997 documentary Tantrums & Tiaras?
8. What was the name of the driver who was killed in the crash that took the life of Princess Diana?

9. Who packed their trunk and said goodbye to the circus?
10. What name is given to a triangle that has three different sides and angles?

Quiz 12

ROUND 1: MUSIC

1. Complete the band name: The Dave Clark...?
2. Roy Wood left Electric Light Orchestra and formed which band?
3. Who was widely referred to as the "Queen of Rock 'n' Roll"?
4. Complete the title of the Nirvana song: Smells Like Teen...?
5. Smooth and Maria Maria were Nineties hits for which group that started life in the late Sixties?

6. Moves Like Jagger was a 2011 hit for Maroon 5 featuring which female singer?
7. Brian, Nick, AJ and Howie make up which boy band?
8. In which country was Rihanna born?
9. What does EP stand for?
10. Who teamed up with Shakira on her hit Hips Don't Lie?

ROUND 2: NATURE

1. Semicircles on a weather map denote which front?
2. What are the two main veins in the neck called?
3. Anaemia is caused by a deficiency of what?
4. What name is given to an adult male swan?
5. What is the name of the enzyme used to break down sugar?
6. What is the plural of mongoose?
7. Nephritis is the inflammation of which organ?
8. What is the highest number on the Beaufort scale?
9. What kind of animal is a Rhodesian Ridgeback?

10. What is the name of the process of growing things in water without soil?

ROUND 3: SPORT

1. In which country would you find the motor racing circuit Gilles Villeneuve?
2. The Indy 500 is completed over how many laps?
3. The Melbourne Cup happens every November in which sport?
4. How many periods are there in an ice hockey game?
5. Lillehammer hosted thc 1994 Winter Olympics, but which country?
6. What sport is played at Roland-Garros?
7. Hitting a single, double and triple of the same number in three darts is known as what?
8. Which animal sits atop of the Calcutta Cup?
9. Which sport has a playing area of 9ft by 5ft?
10. How many yards does an American Football team need to gain to keep moving towards the end zone?

ROUND 4: HISTORY

1. Who was UK Prime Minister for the majority of World War Two?
2. Who was Henry VIII's last wife?
3. 1941 saw what happen for the last time at the Tower of London?
4. Little Boy was the codename given to the bomb dropped where in 1945?
5. The Battle of Agincourt took place in which century?
6. The Crimean War was fought between an alliance including France and Britain against which other nation?
7. What was the codename of the evacuation of Dunkirk?
8. In which year was NATO founded?
9. Who founded the Mongol Empire in 1206?
10. In which country did the Battle of Waterloo take place?

ROUND 5: GEBERAL KNOWLEDGE

1. How many tiles does a player start with in Scrabble?
2. What does the N stand for in the acronym ISBN?
3. The Sundance Kid, Butch Cassidy and Kid Curry made up which gang?
4. Which fictional sport is played on broomsticks?
5. What was the capital of West Germany?
6. Which motor company was previously known as Swallow Sidecar Company?
7. Which fairy-tale character had the ability to turn straw into gold?
8. Which company was founded by Ingvar Kamprad?
9. How many triangular points are on the board of Backgammon?
10. What is the first letter of the Russian alphabet?

Quiz 13

ROUND 1: TV

1. In which soap would you find the Mill Health Centre?
2. Name the sitcom, starting in 1981, that became a nation favourite and saw a spin-off called the Green Green Grass.
3. What is the name of the department store in the sitcom Are You Being Served?
4. The Netflix show Stranger Things is set in which decade?
5. Which gameshow had 22 identical sealed boxes?
6. Where did Puff the Magic Dragon live?
7. The Flintstones live in which fictional town?
8. What name has been given to every Simpsons cat?
9. Who won the first series of American Idol?
10. Who is the alter ego of Dr Banner?

ROUND 2: SCIENCE

1. According to the old tale: Red sky at night, shepherd's delight, red sky in the morning, shepherd's what?
2. Mercury and Venus are the only planets to not have what?
3. Which element has the chemical symbol Pt?
4. What is equal to mass times acceleration?
5. Which astronomer discovered the moons of Jupiter?
6. What mineral is found in pencils?
7. The process of plants turning light into energy is known by which name?
8. Heating up an ore to obtain metal from it is done by which process?
9. In the computer acronym IRL, what does the L stand for?
10. What is another name for junk mail?

ROUND 3: FOOD AND DRINK

1. Vegemite is originally from where?

2. "Made to make your mouth water" was the slogan for which sweet?
3. Pontefract cakes are traditionally made with what?
4. Coconuts and dates grow on what kind of tree?
5. When bread is baked, which gas is produced?
6. Bergamot gives which type of tea its distinctive flavour?
7. In which country would you find the main headquarters of McDonald's?
8. Halloumi cheese originates from which country?
9. What part of farm animals does tripe come from?
10. What food type is Port Salut?

ROUND 4: GEOGRAPHY

1. Which statue stands at 93 metres tall and represents the Roman goddess of freedom?
2. Manhattan, the Bronx, Queens, Brooklyn, and Staten Island make up the five boroughs of where?
3. What is the easternmost county in the UK?
4. What are Krakatoa, Etna and Mauna Loa?

5. What country has the longest coastline in the world?
6. North Korea shares a border with China, South Korea and which other country?
7. Lansing is the capital of which US state?
8. Which is the largest of the Channel Islands?
9. The Khyber Pass links Pakistan and which other country?
10. What is the world's longest mountain range?

ROUND 5: GEBERAL KNOWLEDGE

1. How many candle holders are on a Jewish menorah?
2. According to the nursery rhyme, which child is fair of face?
3. Which city has the world's oldest underground railway system?
4. Who are known as the Inuits?
5. Who wrote The Great Gatsby?
6. What is the more common name for the Euro Tunnel?
7. Who painted the Mona Lisa?

8. Who was the first president of the USA?
9. Co is the chemical symbol for what element?
10. Which country has the most football World Cup wins?

Quiz 14

ROUND 1: FILM

1. Prince William and Harry's secret cameos were cut from which major blockbuster for being too tall?
2. "Frankly, my dear, I don't give a damn." Which classic film?
3. What was the name of Stanley Kubrick 1971 cult classic?
4. Matthew Broderick had the most epic day of his life in which 1986 film?
5. Velma Kelly and Roxie Hart star in which film?

6. Which 1983 movie features the characters Ross Webster and his girlfriend Lorelei Ambrosia?
7. "Check in. Unpack. Relax. Take a shower" was the tagline to which movie?
8. In which James Bond film did the spy go to space?
9. What is the birth name of Darth Vader?
10. What was the name of the child actress who was a number-one box office draw from 1934-1938?

ROUND 2: NATURE

1. What is the medical term Halitosis known as?
2. By what other name might an Alsatian be known?
3. Insulin is produced by which organ?
4. What is the axilla better known as?
5. What is the fastest land animal on two legs?
6. What is the oxygen carrying protein, found in blood, called?
7. The ulna is one of two bones that make up part of what?
8. Which animal has eyes measuring up to 16 inches in diameter?

9. What is the more common name of a keloid on the human body?
10. What part of the body does the inflammation myelitis occur?

ROUND 3: HISTORY

1. In which year did Edward VIII abdicate?
2. Who was Henry VIII's first wife?
3. What important document was signed at Runnymede in 1215?
4. What was the codename for the Normandy landings in World War Two?
5. In Norse mythology, who was the Chief God?
6. How many daughters did Zeus have?
7. Augustus was the great-nephew of which Roman leader?
8. Adolf Hitler was born in which country?
9. Which year did the attack of Pearl Harbour take place?
10. What name was given to the group of campaigners for women to have the right to vote?

ROUND 4: PEOPLE

1. Prince Albert II is the current head of state of which principality?
2. Amelia Earhart set off on her solo transatlantic flight from which Canadian province?
3. Which country was Silvio Berlusconi the former leader of?
4. How is Vincent Damon Furnier better known?
5. In which country was Christopher Columbus born?
6. What was Arthur Jefferson's stage name?
7. Who was assassinated on 24 November 1963?
8. What nationality is Shakira?
9. Charles and Maurice are advertising agency brothers better known by what name?
10. Who was the first person to be made an honorary citizen of the USA?

ROUND 5: GEBERAL KNOWLEDGE

1. Which Japanese word in the English language describes a fold-out bed?

2. What is the accepted capital of Switzerland?
3. What is the most expensive spice in the world?
4. In which year was OJ Simpson cleared of double murder in a trial that captured the world?
5. Solid lava or magma rocks are called what?
6. Who was the Greek goddess of love?
7. Who was the Roman goddess of love?
8. What colour wedge is Geography in Trivial Pursuit?
9. Along with France, which country did Morocco gain independence from in 1956?
10. What is Japanese horseradish better known as?

Quiz 15

ROUND 1: MUSIC

1. Who had Sixties hits with Land Of 1,000 Dances, Funky Broadway and I'm In Love?

2. The song Jessica, made famous as the theme tune to Top Gear, was by which band?
3. Complete the name of the band: Huey Lewis and the...?
4. Which artist recorded Hallelujah, a song covered by artists including Jeff Buckley and Alexandra Burke?
5. Which American singer-songwriter composed the Monkeys hit I'm A Believer?
6. Which group was Justin Timberlake formerly a member of?
7. How is Tramar Dillard better known?
8. Who did Queen ask to do the fandango in the song Bohemian Rhapsody?
9. Whose first UK number-one single was It's All Over Now?
10. David Robert Jones is better known as which English singer-songwriter and actor?

ROUND 2: SPORT

1. The Dark Destroyer was the nickname of which boxer?
2. In which sport do opponents flip a coin to win the match?

3. At which racecourse does the Kentucky Derby take place?
4. In which sport is there a face-off to start the game?
5. What is the first Grand Slam tennis event of the year?
6. Oklahoma Thunder, Miami Heat and Memphis Grizzlies all play which sport?
7. The six-tackle rule is an important rule in which sport?
8. Which three countries will host the 2026 football World Cup?
9. Roger Bannister became the first person to run a mile in under what in 1954?
10. In which country was John McEnroe born?

ROUND 3: ART AND LITERATURE

1. What talk show host wrote the autobiography entitled I'm Only Being Honest?
2. Peter Susan Edmund and Lucy are characters in which book series?
3. What was the first name of the scientist Frankenstein?

4. Who wrote Watership Down?
5. Which fictional bear comes from Peru?
6. Who wrote Around The World In 80 Days?
7. In which city did Anne Frank write her famous diary?
8. Who painted the Hay Wain?
9. Which author created the characters Jeeves, Bertie Wooster and Psmith?
10. Which bird was used as croquet mallets in Alice In Wonderland?

ROUND 4: GEOGRAPHY

1. What is the capital city of Malaysia?
2. Pho and banh mi are dishes from which country?
3. What British town got its name from the proximity to the cam river?
4. What is the longest river in Asia?
5. Which English city has more miles of canals than Venice?
6. What are the three colours on the Dutch flag?

7. Which country's currency was the lira before it changed to the euro?
8. How many stars are on the flag of the EU?
9. In which country would you find the White Heron Castle?
10. In which country would you find Louis Armstrong Airport?

ROUND 5: GEBERAL KNOWLEDGE

1. Who wrote and created Jurassic Park?
2. Aviators Wilbur and Orville were better known as what brothers?
3. In which country would you find Mount Kilimanjaro?
4. What is the sixth letter of the Greek alphabet?
5. What is traditionally given on a 45th wedding anniversary?
6. What was the name given to the first cloned sheep?
7. The Herald of Free Enterprise capsized near which port in 1987?
8. What was Romeo's family name in Romeo and Juliet?

9. Roman numerals: How many letters are in use to replace the numbers?

10. How many stars are on the flag of Australia?

Quiz 16

ROUND 1: TV

1. What kind of business would you associate with the TV show Crossroads?

2. What was the name of the holiday camp in Hi-De-Hi?

3. Ashes To Ashes was the spin-off to which TV series?

4. John Fashanu and Ulrika Jonsson were the original presenters on which physical-based gameshow?

5. Set in the fictional town of Newtown, name the police drama that ran for 801 episodes between 1962 and 1978.

6. Which former Coronation Street actress starred as

Catherine Cawood in Happy Valley?

7. When Janet Met Jonny was a musical episode in which TV comedy?
8. Jerry Seinfeld played which character in Seinfeld?
9. Which of these was not a judge on the original Pop Idol: Will Young, Simon Cowell, Neil Fox?
10. Larkhall Prison was the setting for which TV prison drama?

ROUND 2: SCIENCE

1. What was the famous equation that Albert Einstein came up with?
2. Which planet has moons named Iapetus, Rhea and Titan?
3. A day on Venus is longer than a year. True or false?
4. What is the star Sirius better known as?
5. What does C stand for in LCD?
6. Which chemical element is represented by P
7. What part of the Earth sits below the crust?
8. Which element are diamonds a form of?

9. What is bigger, a meteor or an asteroid?
10. Frank Whittle is credited with inventing what?

ROUND 3: PEOPLE

1. In 2016, who ran the London Marathon from the international space station?
2. Simon Weston became famous for his courage following horrific injuries during which war?
3. Which monarch was the main target for Guy Fawkes?
4. Which singer's surname is Ciccone?
5. Actor Laurence Tureaud is better known by what name?
6. Sarah Hugill, Sarah Brightman and Madeleine Gurdon have been married to which composer?
7. Which country is Scott Morrison the Prime Minister of?
8. Who was the last British Prime Minister of the 20th century?
9. With which sport was Bernie Ecclestone the long-time boss?
10. How is Paul Reubens better known?

ROUND 4: PLACES

1. Which party island has an airport called Aeroport d'Eivissa?
2. What is the capital of Venezuela?
3. The Millau Viaduct is the tallest what in the world?
4. Which country comes last in all lists alphabetically?
5. What is the capital of North Korea?
6. In which country would you find Machu Picchu?
7. The River Tagus flows through Spain to which other European capital city?
8. In which country would you find Robben Island?
9. In which sea would you find the Cayman Islands?
10. The Yukon River flows through Canada into which US state?

ROUND 5: GEBERAL KNOWLEDGE

1. Which category would you have won if you have a green wedge in Trivial Pursuit?
2. The interior angles of a triangle always equal what?
3. Which American state come first alphabetically?

4. Bruce Willis, Goldie Hawn and Meryl Streep starred in which 1992 film: Death Becomes...?
5. What is the correct name for antifreeze?
6. Wilma is the cartoon wife of whom?
7. In the nursery rhyme, what was Friday's child?
8. In an SLR camera, what does the R stand for?
9. Dong is the currency of which country?
10. Which country's flag has the colours, from left to right, black, yellow and red?

Quiz 17

ROUND 1: FILM

1. Nicolas Cage swapped faces with whom in the movie Face/Off?
2. In which film does a young widow find her late husband left her 10 messages to help ease her pain?
3. Name the 1994 cult classic that starred Bruce Willis, Samuel L Jackson, John Travolta and Uma Thurman?
4. Despite Deadpool being a massive success, what was the previous Ryan Reynolds superhero movie that flopped in 2011?
5. What was the first name of Bourne, played by Matt Damon?
6. Who starred as John Kimble, an undercover policeman working in a kindergarten?
7. "I carried a watermelon" is a line from which Eighties classic movie?
8. Emmet and Wyldstyle were characters in which toy-inspired animated movie?

9. Who plays Harry Potter in the movies?
10. Which movie starts with a voiceover from Hugh Grant talking about the arrivals area at Heathrow Airport?

ROUND 2: NATURE

1. What is the epidermis?
2. How many legs does a crab have?
3. Patella is the scientific name for which body part?
4. Rhinoceros horns' are made of keratin. True or false?
5. Where in the body would you find the carotid artery?
6. The part of the body between the head and rib cage is described as what?
7. A normal human has how many pairs of ribs?
8. What pandemic in the 14th century claimed the lives of millions of people?
9. What animal can be giant, red or lesser?
10. Epistaxis is bleeding from which part of the body?

ROUND 3: ART AND LITERATURE

1. In Roald Dahl's book, who does George make his marvellous medicine for?
2. Who wrote the Adrian Mole books?
3. Jack Piggy and Ralph are the three central characters in which book?
4. What does Johann Strauss opera Die Fledermaus translate to in English?
5. What pen name does David John Moore Cornwell write under?
6. Who wrote The Three Musketeers?
7. Which part of a stage in a theatre is furthest from the audience?
8. Who wrote the novel of Ben-Hur?
9. What is Edvard Munch's most famous painting?
10. Who wrote the operas William Tell and The Barber Of Seville?

ROUND 4: HISTORY

1. What was the name of the company that operated the Titanic?

2. Where was the first British colony in America?
3. In which year did Graham Alexander Bell invent the telephone?
4. Marie Curie discovered radium and polonium, but what did she name polonium after?
5. Who was British Prime Minister when Queen Elizabeth II was coronated?
6. The Battle of El Alamein took place in which country during World War Two?
7. How many people have walked on the moon?
8. David Scott and James Irwin were the first two people to drive where?
9. In which century did the Spanish Armada attack Britain?
10. Pharaohs were rulers of which ancient country?

ROUND 5: GEBERAL KNOWLEDGE

1. What nationality was Pythagoras, famous for his theorems?
2. What was Princess Diana's maiden name?
3. Which country in the world has the largest population with Spanish as their native language?

4. Bolivia and Paraguay are landlocked countries on which continent?
5. The kroon was the currency of which country before swapping to the euro?
6. In space, "no one can hear you scream" is the tagline to which movie?
7. Which alcoholic drink is made from fermented pears?
8. What is the name of a flat-bottomed venetian rowing boat, seen on the canals of Venice?
9. France, Spain and Morocco are unique in that they share coastlines with which two bodies of water?
10. Who played Annie Wilkes in Misery?

Quiz 18

ROUND 1: MUSIC

1. Whose 1967 debut album was entitled The Piper At The Gates Of Dawn?
2. With which band would you associate Paul Stanley, Gene Simmons, Eric Singer and Tommy Thayer?
3. Which duo's biggest UK hit was Maneater in 1982?
4. All That Matters To Me was a hit for whom in 1992?
5. Which American singer was married to Nancy Barbato, Ava Gardner, Mia Farrow and Barbara Marx?
6. What was the name of the group fronted by Gloria Estefan?
7. Frank Sinatra, Dean Martin and Sammy Davis Jr among others were unofficially known collectively as what?
8. Complete the band name: Creedence Clearwater...?
9. Whose final UK single before their death was Jealous Guy?

10. Cheryl James and Sandra Denton are better known as which hip-hop group?

ROUND 2: FOOD AND DRINK

1. Kids and grown-ups love them so, the happy world of which sweet?
2. Ciabatta bread originates in which country?
3. Cabbage is the main ingredient of which German national dish?
4. In blue cheese, what is the blue part?
5. Asahi is a beer from which country?
6. What is the chemical element that you would find in cheese and milk?
7. What is a courgette also known as?
8. Little Tongues is the English translation of which pasta type?
9. Rich Tea, Nice and Digestive are all types of what?
10. "You only get an oo" with which brand of tea, according to the advert?

ROUND 3: SPORT

1. The Grand National horse race is held at which UK racetrack?
2. Charles Barkley, Patrick Ewing and Allen Iverson are all Hall of Fame inductees in which sport?
3. Which track and field event involves using a pole to jump over a bar?
4. Which Olympic sport covers the longest distance?
5. How many people are in the boat of a rowing eight crew?
6. The first international cricket match was between USA and Canada. True or false?
7. Which winter sport sees competitors head down an icy track feet first with no brakes?
8. How many colours are in the Olympic rings?
9. What nationality was Martina Navratilova?
10. Who was England manager before Fabio Capello?

ROUND 4: GEOGRAPHY

1. Which country shares borders with the following: Afghanistan, China, India and Iran?

2. What river flows through Paris?
3. What ocean is home to the Mariana Trench?
4. How many US states border the Pacific Ocean?
5. What is the world's largest man-made structure?
6. The Seychelles are located in which ocean?
7. Tampa, Orlando and Jacksonville are cities in which US state?
8. Which is the largest of the Scandinavian countries by area?
9. What water separates Africa and Europe?
10. Dracula famously lived in the historical region of Transylvania – but in what country would you now find his castle?

ROUND 5: GEBERAL KNOWLEDGE

1. What does the word cenotaph translate to?
2. What kind of transport was the Orient Express?
3. In terms of computing, what does the L stand for in LAN?
4. What colour light indicates the port side of a plane or boat?

5. What is the name of clarified butter used in Indian cooking?
6. Which islands are also known as Islas Malvinas?
7. On which continent would you find the river Rhone?
8. According to the nursery rhyme, who killed Cock Robin?
9. And what weapon did they use?
10. What did Thursday's child have, according to the nursery rhyme?

Quiz 19

ROUND 1: MUSIC

1. Glendarroch was the name of the fictional village in which UK soap opera?
2. Which long-running sitcom, which launched in 1988, had characters including Cat, Holly and Kryten?

3. Complete the name of the American police comedy: Brooklyn...?
4. Which girl group launched Channel 5 on its opening night?
5. Running for 10 series on ITV starting in 1988, name the gameshow presented by Bruce Forsyth, Matthew Kelly and Darren Day, where contestants completed challenges against the clock.
6. Polly, Pamela, Alan, Terry and Kevin were the parents' names in which comedy?
7. Who played Michael Knight in Knight Rider?
8. Wo Fat was a regular villain in which TV series?
9. What is the name of the police chief in The Simpsons?
10. Who was the original host of Supermarket Sweep?

ROUND 2: ART AND LITERATURE

1. Where does Winnie the Pooh live?
2. The Man In The White Suit was a book by Ben Collins, featuring stories about his time as whom?
3. How many tales make up the Canterbury Tales?

4. "I paint objects as I think them, not as I see them" is a famous quote attributed to which painter?
5. Which famous cloth tells the story of the Battle of Hastings among others?
6. Which author wrote under the pen name George Eliot?
7. What are H.G. Wells' first and middle names?
8. Who created the character of Jason Bourne?
9. The character of Percy Blakeney is better known by which name?
10. Which author wrote Lady Chatterley's Lover?

ROUND 3: HISTORY

1. Utah, Omaha, Gold, Juno and Sword were the allied code name for beaches in which World War Two invasion?
2. Who replaced Tony Blair as Prime Minister?
3. What was the name of Lord Nelson's flagship at the Battle of Trafalgar?
4. Which two kingdoms fought in the battle of Stamford Bridge?

5. What was the departure point for the final fateful flight of the Hindenburg?
6. John Rockefeller became the world's first billionaire in which decade?
7. Complete the name of the famous documents found in Palestine: The Dead Sea...?
8. What is the name of the town in the USA that became synonymous with UFO conspiracies?
9. Who were the two main combatants of the Hundred Years War?
10. A hoax photograph from 1934 gave rise to which mythical monster in Scotland?

ROUND 4: PLACES

1. The Three Peaks challenge is made up of Ben Nevis, Snowdon and which other?
2. What is the capital of Turkey?
3. What is the largest city in the USA in terms of population?
4. In which country would you find Copacabana beach?
5. Vienna is on which river?

6. What is the capital of Argentina?
7. Which country did Belgium declare independence from in 1830?
8. In which country would you find Colditz Castle?
9. In which modern-day country would you find the UNESCO site of Persepolis?
10. What is the longest river in Canada?

ROUND 5: GEBERAL KNOWLEDGE

1. What is the name given to the cold soup dish traditionally from Spain?
2. Which newspaper did Clark Kent work for?
3. Who wrote Moby Dick?
4. What was written underneath the words Titanic on the doomed ship?
5. What word beginning with F describes someone winning by chance?
6. Chlorophyll gives leaves what colour?
7. In which decade was the Empire State Building opened?
8. What fruit is used in the liqueur Kirsch?

9. In which country would you find the iconic Marina Bay Sands?

10. What does HB on a pencil stand for?

Quiz 20

ROUND 1: FILM

1. "Roads? Where we are going, we don't need roads." Name the film.

2. Keira Knightley appeared in which Jane Austen book turned film?

3. "Feed me, Seymour!" is from which 1986 film?

4. "Show me the money" is from which movie?

5. Jack Traven is the lead character in which 1994 blockbuster movie?

6. Mike Myers provides the voice for which Ogre?

7. Who was the original voice of Bugs Bunny, Daffy

Duck, Porky Pig and many others?

8. Name the 1978 superhero film starring Gene Hackman, Marlon Brando and Christopher Reeve?
9. Mr White, Mr Brown and Mr Orange are characters in which movie?
10. Jodie Foster, Bonnie Langford and Dexter Fletcher all starred in which 1976 gangster musical comedy film?

ROUND 2: SCIENCE

1. Which planet is named after the Roman messenger to the gods?
2. An oxygen-starved fire that then explodes when oxygen is re-introduced is known as a what?
3. What is the chemical symbol of Argon?
4. The Einstein-Rosen bridge, well known in physics around time travel, is known by what nickname?
5. Who invented dynamite?
6. What is the pH level for pure water?
7. In which city would you find the Juventus football team?

8. What is the phenomenon called when the moon passes between the Earth and the sun?
9. What is the main gas in the Earth's atmosphere?
10. What is the substance used to create guitar picks?

ROUND 3: SPORT

1. In which sport would you find the Fed Cup?
2. The Pumas is the nickname for which country's rugby union team?
3. Which family bought Manchester United in 2005?
4. Wenlock and Mandeville were the mascots of which Olympic Games?
5. How many hurdles are jumped in the 110-metre race?
6. To score a perfect game in ten-pin bowling, how many strikes are needed?
7. Who was the first unseeded player to win Wimbledon?
8. Zara Philips is married to which former rugby player?
9. Which football clubs fans did Delia Smith famously ask where they were at half-time?

10. The Copa Libertadores is which continent's version of the Champions League?

ROUND 4: PEOPLE

1. Which country is Justin Trudeau the leader of?
2. Who was known as the Angel of Death during World War Two?
3. Charles Babbage is credited with inventing the first what?
4. How is Erik Weisz better known?
5. Courtney Love was married to whom, just before his tragic death in 1994?
6. Priscilla Chan is the wife of which social media CEO?
7. Which controversial figure was the creator of the website Wikileaks?
8. Who was born Allan Stewart Konigsberg?
9. Eva Peron was the president of which country?
10. What is the name of the playwright that was said to have greatly influenced William Shakespeare?

ROUND 5: GEBERAL KNOWLEDGE

1. What colour, traditionally, is an Indian wedding sari?
2. Pestilence, War, Famine and Death make up the four what?
3. In terms of ships, what does RMS stand for?
4. Which of the seven dwarfs has the shortest name?
5. Gynophobia is a fear of what?
6. What was Wednesday's child according to the nursery rhyme?
7. The G7 became the G8 when which country joined, and which has subsequently left?
8. What is the better known name for hook and loop fastening?
9. Captives who show empathy for their captors are known to suffer from which syndrome?
10. In which South American country would you find Sugarloaf Mountain?

Quiz 21

ROUND 1: MUSIC

1. Which of these Roy Orbison hits – Oh, Pretty Woman; It's Over; You Got It – failed to make number one in the UK charts?
2. What was the name of the American punk rock band who had hits with Rock 'N' Roll High School and Sheena Is A Punk Rocker?
3. Annie Lennox and Dave Stewart were known by which name?
4. Stay Another Day was a Christmas number one in 1994 for which band?
5. The UK rhythm and blues/rock band The Animals were formed in which UK city?
6. What weekday is repeated in the title of a 1966 hit for the 'Mamas And Papas'?
7. Who had a hit in the Seventies with Ain't No Mountain High Enough?
8. Who had a hit with Vertigo in 2004?

9. I Have Confidence and Do-Re-Mi are songs from which musical?
10. With which band was Gwen Stefani the lead singer?

ROUND 2: NATURE

1. The dingo is a free range dog found in which country?
2. What is the name given to the medical condition whereby dizziness is experienced due to heights?
3. White Plague or White Death is better known by which medical name?
4. Where on the body would you find the philtrum?
5. Dementia is the most common form of which disease?
6. A rhytidectomy procedure is more commonly known as a what?
7. Are frogs warm or cold blooded?
8. What is arachnophobia a fear of?
9. How many bones does a shark have?
10. By what acronym is Deoxyribonucleic acid better known?

ROUND 3: FOOD AND DRINK

1. Bratwurst is the German word for which type of food?
2. Worcester sauce is traditionally added to which cocktail drink?
3. What was known as the mint with a hole?
4. What sauce is traditionally served with lamb?
5. Pink Lady, Jazz and Gala are all types of what?
6. Roti is another name for which popular Italian flatbread?
7. What is the alcoholic base for a White Russian?
8. One of the biggest robberies in UK history, at Hatton Garden, took place over which holiday weekend?
9. A Margarita has which main alcoholic component?
10. Caramelized sugar and butter traditionally makes which sweet treat?

ROUND 4: GEOGRAPHY

1. Which European capital city is served by Arlanda Airport?
2. How many US states begin with the letter A?
3. What is the largest UK city without a professional football team?
4. What is the most abundant metal found in the Earth's crust?
5. Which European capital was built across 14 islands?
6. What is the capital city of New Zealand?
7. Stretching over 1,900 miles, what is the name of the mountain range that runs from New Mexico to British Columbia?
8. Name one of the three countries that share a land border with more than 10 other countries.
9. What is the largest US state by land area?
10. What is Spain's largest island?

ROUND 5: GEBERAL KNOWLEDGE

1. What colour wedge is Entertainment in Trivial Pursuit?
2. Columbia University give out what annual award for achievements in Newspaper and Literature?
3. The tallest building in Africa is the Carlton Centre, but in which country would you find it?
4. The large gathering of scouts is known as a what?
5. The Zonda sports car is made by which manufacturer?
6. What does the G stand for in 3G, 4G and 5G in terms of mobile communications?
7. Skull Island is the fictional home of which large animal?
8. How many dance styles are in the phonetic alphabet?
9. Which country's secret service is known as Mossad?
10. Native to Jamaica, what is the name of the hot spice traditionally found on chicken?

Quiz 22

ROUND 1: TV

1. Nicholas Lyndhurst played a time-travelling TV repair man in which sitcom?
2. Cheers is the bar where everybody knows what?
3. Michael Aspel took over presenting This is Your Life from which host?
4. Gripper, Zammo and Tucker Jenkins were all characters in which children's TV show?
5. Gerry and Sylvia Anderson created which puppets?
6. Who played Richie Cunningham in Happy Days?
7. What was the name of Zippy's big bear friend?
8. Ricky Gervais played the character Andy Millman in which TV series?
9. What does the acronym TOWIE stand for?
10. Which quiz show involves a giant penny-dropping machine?

ROUND 2: SPORT

1. How many teams have played in every season of the Premier League since its inception?
2. Uneven bars and balance beam are disciplines in which female leisure and sport pursuit?
3. In which sport would you stand at the oche?
4. Long and short corners are a feature of which sport?
5. Which sport requires a shuttlecock?
6. Which sport takes place in a velodrome?
7. In which city would you find Lansdowne Road Stadium?
8. What is the name of the short version of rugby that appears at the Olympics?
9. Which England manager has a record of played one, won one?
10. In what sport is Michael Phelps a famous name?

ROUND 3: HISTORY

1. What was the name of the ship that was first to appear on the scene after the sinking of the Titanic?

2. How many of Henry VIII's children became monarchs?
3. William the Conqueror led who to victory at the Battle of Hastings?
4. In which decade did Edmund Hillary and Tenzing Norgay reach the summit of Everest?
5. What was the name of the nuclear power plant destroyed in the earthquake in Japan 2011?
6. Which American president shouted "tear down this wall!" in 1987?
7. What was the name of the treaty signed at the end of World War One?
8. In which decade was the Wall Street Crash that led to the Great Depression?
9. Who did Prince Edward marry in 1999?
10. What was the 6 June 1944 better known as?

ROUND 4: SCIENCE

1. What is the name of the paper used to test for acid or alkalis?
2. Which planet has Ganymede, the largest moon in the solar system?

3. A Snellen chart tests what?
4. In computing terms, what is Linux?
5. What is the chemical symbol of Uranium?
6. The Big Dipper is made up of how many stars?
7. What is the more common name for dyspepsia?
8. What is the medical term for Siamese twins?
9. Copper and zinc make up alloy what?
10. What is another name for the medicine, acetylsalicylic acid?

ROUND 5: GEBERAL KNOWLEDGE

1. In which country would you find the Vasco da Gama Bridge?
2. Who makes the Veyron car?
3. Which is the largest country contained wholly inside Europe?
4. What is the more common name for the festival known as Fat Tuesday?
5. British Honduras became which country after gaining independence?

6. What kind of transport device is a Chinook?
7. A jeroboam is equivalent to how many standard bottles?
8. The Taj Mahal was built in which century?
9. Which mobile game turned film sees birds trying to defeat pigs?
10. In which country would you find the Parthenon Acropolis?

Quiz 23

ROUND 1: FILM

1. What were the colours of the pills in the Matrix?
2. Who played the Green Fairy in Moulin Rouge?
3. Damn it, Janet; Sweet Transvestite and Time Warp are songs that can be found in which film?
4. Field Of Dreams is based on which sport?

5. In which musical would you find the characters Jenny Lind, Phillip Carlyle and Anne Wheeler?
6. Which Bond film did Billie Eilish write the theme tune to?
7. Ralph Macchio, Elisabeth Shue and Pat Morita star in which 1984 martial arts film?
8. Where was the movie The Full Monty set?
9. In which musical would you find the song Cell Block Tango?
10. Julia Roberts won best actress at the Academy Awards for playing which character?

ROUND 2: NATURE

1. One For Sorrow, Two For Joy is nursery rhyme connected with superstition around which bird?
2. A group of dolphins are called a what?
3. Which part of the body is affected by emphysema?
4. What tree has a variety called weeping?
5. What are the birds said to protect the Tower of London?
6. Mycology is the study of what?

7. What is the name of the oath taken by doctors?
8. How many wings does a bee have?
9. Which mythical bird is said to die and then be reborn from the ashes?
10. How many valves make up the human heart?

ROUND 3: ART AND LITERATURE

1. In the Bible, which has more books, the Old Testament or the New?
2. What is the name of Hansel's sister in the fairy tales?
3. Which gallery houses the Mona Lisa?
4. Which author wrote The Borrowers?
5. Who wrote Black Beauty?
6. Who created Peter Rabbit?
7. Who wrote the controversial Satanic Verses?
8. "A horse! A horse! My kingdom for a horse!" is from which Shakespeare play?
9. Who wrote The Silence Of The Lambs?
10. Who wrote Catcher In The Rye?

ROUND 4: PEOPLE

1. Who was Queen Elizabeth I's mother?
2. Who is Neville John Holder better known as?
3. Andrew Holness is the Prime Minister of which country?
4. Fred Durst was the lead singer with which group?
5. How were PJ & Duncan better known?
6. Which actress was born Frances Ethel Gumm?
7. Which campaigner was shot in Memphis in 1968?
8. Which famous actor is father to Angelina Jolie?
9. With which band would you associate Stevie Nicks and Peter Green?
10. Which actor was born Archibald Leach in 1904?

ROUND 5: GEBERAL KNOWLEDGE

1. What is the main ingredient in guacamole?
2. In which country would you find Mount Elbrus?
3. Al Forna in Italian cooking means it has been cooked how?

4. Lake Eyre is the largest lake in which country?
5. What was the name of the Dodge Charger in The Dukes Of Hazzard?
6. When a new Pope is elected what smoke is blown from the chimney?
7. What type of food is mange tout?
8. How many deadly sins are there?
9. What fruit makes the syrup grenadine?
10. What is the name of the giant seaway in Canada and North America that allows vessels to pass into the great lakes?

Quiz 24

ROUND 1: MUSIC

1. Which legendary duo's first names were Paul and Art?
2. John McVie and Stevie Nicks are members of which group?
3. Which Sisters had hits with Automatic and Jump?
4. Who said everybody wanted to rule the world, according to the title of their Eighties song?
5. Surfin, Surfin Safari and Surfin USA were Sixties hits for which group?
6. What was the name of the LeAnn Rimes hit which featured in the movie Coyote Ugly?
7. Which singer formed The Style Council after leaving The Jam?
8. What night did Whigfield sing about?
9. What nationality were Roxette?
10. What card game features in the title of a 2008 Lady Gaga song?

ROUND 2: SCIENCE

1. What is the wire inside a light bulb called?
2. What was the name of the British spacecraft that crashed on Mars in 2003?
3. What chemical element has the symbol Cl?
4. Which chemical is said to be contained in acid rain?
5. Which chemical element has the symbol Li?
6. What is the rarest blood type?
7. Which planet completes one rotation in just 10 hours?
8. You can hear sounds in space. True or false?
9. CFCs were banned in the Seventies because they were causing damage to which layer?
10. How many inches are in a hand?

ROUND 3: FOOD AND DRINK

1. Arctic Roll was made up of sponge, raspberry sauce and what other main ingredient?
2. Beef and Tomato, Chicken and Mushroom and Bombay Bad Boy are flavours of what kind of quick snack/meal?

3. A Bakewell tart has what on top?
4. Clam chowder originated from which country?
5. Sparkling wine labelled brut means it is what?
6. Name the Scottish dish usually boiled in an animal's stomach?
7. Gin and vermouth makes up which drink?
8. Cheese and which other ingredient make up a croque-monsieur sandwich?
9. In Asian cooking, what is a tandoor?
10. Bergamot is used to flavour which type of tea?

ROUND 4: GEOGRAPHY

1. Which country has a larger total area, Canada, Russia or the USA?
2. On the London Tube network, which is the only station to begin with the letter I?
3. What Turkish city shares its name with a superhero?
4. Sicily is the largest island in which sea?
5. Alaska is the largest state in America, but what is the second largest?

6. How many times zones does Russia have?
7. What tourist destination would you find at the junction of Broadway and Seventh Avenue?
8. With how many countries does Spain share a land border?
9. Which European river flows from Switzerland to the Netherlands?
10. Which continent is home to the Pensacola Mountains?

ROUND 5: GEBERAL KNOWLEDGE

1. Which island of Indonesia is the most populated?
2. How many years is a Platinum Jubilee?
3. Which country's flag has a yellow cross on a black and green background?
4. Mont Blanc is the highest mountain in which range?
5. What is the next prime number in this sequence: 11,13,17...?
6. How many in a baker's dozen?
7. Islamabad is the capital city of which country?
8. In which country does paella originate?

9. Suleiman the Magnificent was the ruler of which empire?
10. Who represented the UK at Eurovision with the song Congratulations?

Quiz 25

ROUND 1: TV

1. What is Doctor Who's time box called?
2. What were the names of Neil Morrissey's and Martin Clunes' characters in Men Behaving Badly?
3. Sheldon Cooper was the lead character in which TV comedy?
4. Who presented the original run of the Krypton Factor?
5. Pricing up products is a key element of which TV gameshow?

6. With which TV show would you find the song Smelly Cat?
7. Which TV series had the numbers 90210 in the title?
8. Which Python took the lead role in Fawlty Towers?
9. What is the name of the dating show presented by Anna Richardson?
10. Which TV series featured the character PC David Budd?

ROUND 2: NATURE

1. What kind of animal was Chi Chi, who became "England's best-loved zoo animal"?
2. Goldfinch, Collared Dove and Starling are all types of what?
3. What is the name of the main muscle separating the chest from the abdomen?
4. What is the tallest species of penguin?
5. What does a person studying ichthyology study?
6. What part of the body is removed during a glossectomy operation?

7. HDL and LDL measure what in the blood stream?
8. What species of ape is the closest to humans?
9. Which animal is sometimes called a land beaver, whistle pig or woodchuck?
10. Which organ regulates the level of salt and water in the blood?

ROUND 3: ART AND LITERATURE

1. Which author wrote Deception Point, The Lost Symbol and Angels And Demons?
2. Who sculptured the statue David?
3. Georges Braque and which other artist are credited with co-founding the cubism movement?
4. Who wrote the book More Fool Me: A Memoir?
5. Whose autobiography was published 100 years after his death?
6. The Last Battle completes which novel series?
7. Who committed the first-ever murder, according to the Bible?
8. Who wrote Wind In The Willows?

9. Complete the Shakespeare quote: "Friends, Romans, countrymen..."?
10. Rembrandt painted the Night what?

ROUND 4: PLACES

1. Three countries are completely landlocked by one other country, San Marino, Vatican City and which other?
2. In which countries would you find Victoria Falls?
3. What bright light city would you find in the Mojave Desert?
4. Ecuador and Chile are the only two countries in South America that do not border which other nation?
5. What is the world's most northern capital city?
6. What is the smallest country in the world by area at only .44 of a kilometre?
7. Bridgetown is the capital of which island?
8. Catalonia is a region in which country?
9. Which European river flows from Switzerland to the Netherlands?

10. The island of Borneo is divided among three countries: Brunei, Malaysia and which other?

ROUND 5: GEBERAL KNOWLEDGE

1. Crème de Cassis liqueur is flavoured with which fruit?
2. How many signs of the zodiac are there?
3. Warsaw is the capital city of which country?
4. A 20th anniversary is celebrated with what traditionally?
5. What hard Italian cheese is made from ewe's milk?
6. In which country would you find Bethlehem?
7. Which car-maker manufactured the Diablo supercar?
8. The Tropic of Cancer is north or south of the equator?
9. In which country would you find the forbidden city?
10. What is the smallest of the US states?

Quiz 26: Children's Quiz 1

1. Tower Bridge is in which English city?
2. What is the name of the app that has gone viral that allows you to record short lip-sync videos, and that adults have been embarrassing their kids with?
3. Putting your arm across your face and another one in the air is called doing a what?
4. In which film would you find the dragon Toothless?
5. What is the art of paper folding called?
6. What happened in London in 1666?
7. Who has an aeroplane called Air Force One?
8. What is the name of the baby in the Simpsons?
9. Goldilocks had an encounter with how many bears?
10. What is Pepper Pig's little brother called?
11. Where does solar power come from?
12. How many days are there in a leap year?
13. What is the name of the gas that makes balloons float?

14. What was the name of the digger in Bob The Builder?
15. What was Super Mario's job?
16. What machine would you put your clothes in to wash them?
17. What is the name of the person who protects you at the swimming pool?
18. What was the name of the Minions' boss?
19. Which berries would you find in Ribena?
20. What is 10% of 1,000?
21. What was the name of the hoover in Teletubbies?
22. How many rings make up the Olympic symbol?
23. What is the smallest value coin we have?
24. What is the name of the school in Harry Potter?
25. Who sat on a wall, before he had a great fall?
26. What is the main type of animal in the Jurassic Park film series?
27. Which fairy might give you money if something came out of your mouth?
28. Which cartoon character asks Can We Fix It?

29. What must all the angles of the square add up to?
30. Who makes the iPad?
31. In which place might you get a Happy Meal?
32. How many people do you need to make a see-saw work properly?
33. What is the name of a game where you need to put pieces together to make a picture?
34. In which book series did you need to find the same character on each page?
35. Which animal mainly gives us milk?
36. Where is a watch normally worn?
37. What kind of transport might you need to travel on water?
38. What is the capital of Germany?
39. What is the name of the bear that supports Children In Need?
40. What is the name of the baddie on Doctor Who that keeps saying "exterminate"?
41. According to the rhyme, Round And Round The Garden, like a what?
42. What colour is Dory in Finding Nemo?

43. In which country would you find the pyramids?
44. In what street does the Prime Minister of the UK live on?
45. What countries make up the UK?
46. What would you call your parent's sister?
47. How many letters are there in the alphabet?
48. What is the name of the exams you might take before you leave school at 16 years old?
49. Finish the saying from the Simpsons, "Hi everybody..."?
50. Who was Harry Potter's two best friends?

Quiz 27: Children's Quiz 2

1. What vegetable makes would you need to make mash?
2. What is H2O known as?
3. What time of year would you traditionally eat hot cross buns?

4. What does 'lol' stand for?
5. How many sides does a triangle have?
6. What is a baby cat called?
7. Who might say the words, "What's up, doc?"
8. Lightning McQueen is in which movie?
9. Jesy, Perrie, Jade and Leigh-Anne are in which pop group?
10. Change 0.5 into a fraction.
11. Crawl, backstroke and butterfly can be found in what fitness exercise?
12. How many sides does a hexagon have?
13. Which planet is known as the Red Planet?
14. Cheryl Cole used to sing in which famous girl band?
15. How many years are there in one century?
16. Which continent is India in?
17. How many hours are there in seven days?
18. How many blind mice were there?
19. What is the Earth's primary source of energy?
20. What does 'www' stand for?
21. Which Prince is next to be King in the UK?

22. What does a thermometer measure?
23. What were the name of Willy Wonka's helpers in Charlie And The Chocolate Factory?
24. What is a non-magical person called in Harry Potter?
25. Christopher Robbin was in which book series?
26. In Hey Diddle Diddle, what ran away with the spoon?
27. What are the seven dwarfs digging for in Snow White?
28. Which skeleton in the human body protects the brain?
29. If I put water into the freezer and left it for a few hours, what would I get?
30. What is the first chemical element on the periodic table?
31. Who was behind the Gunpowder Plot?
32. Arteries carry what away from the heart?
33. Plants use photosynthesis to make their own what?
34. Metals are good conductors. True or false?
35. What is 11 x 33?

36. How many men did the Grand Old Duke of York have?
37. Who was sitting in a corner eating his curds and whey?
38. What ran up the clock in Hickory Dickory Dock?
39. What did Jack break when he fell down the hill?
40. And 20 blackbirds where baked into a pie in which nursery rhyme?
41. How many visible colours are there in the rainbow? And can you name them for extra points?
42. Who is Minnie Mouse's boyfriend?
43. In which film series would you find Donkey, Pinocchio and Princess Fiona?
44. Which joint connects the leg to the foot?
45. Pikachu can be found in which game?
46. Father Christmas lives at which pole?
47. Gordon, James Henry and Percy are what kind of vehicle?
48. Who had a cat named Pilchard?
49. What is Spiderman's real name?
50. If a bicycle has two wheels, how many does a unicycle?

Quiz 28: Children's Quiz 3

1. How many zeros are there in ten thousand?
2. How many weeks in three years?
3. What is the name of George Pig's sister?
4. What is the tallest animal in the world?
5. Which comic character turns green when he gets mad?
6. How many pockets are there on a snooker table?
7. Which fairy tale character slept for 100 years?
8. What is a baby goat called?
9. Hedwig the owl belonged to whom?
10. There is an invisible line that runs around the middle of the Earth – what is it called?
11. Captain Hook was whose enemy?
12. Who lost her sheep in the nursery rhymes?
13. If I performed a slam dunk, what sport would I be playing?
14. In Snow White And The Seven Dwarves, Doc was

the only one who wore glasses. True or false?

15. Noah took how many of each animal on to the ark?
16. Where would you mainly find a narrowboat?
17. Which online game begining with R allows users the ability to program and play user-created games?
18. Who was the leader of the Merry Men?
19. The Leaning Tower Of Pisa is in which country?
20. Porsche is a type of what?
21. Who is Bart, Lisa and Maggie's mother?
22. How many symbols in a row do you need to win a game of noughts and crosses?
23. In which sport might you make a try?
24. In the nursery rhyme, what kind of place did Old Macdonald have?
25. Alfred was a butler for which superhero?
26. Who was Sonic the Hedgehog's best friend?
27. Who sang the song Lego House?
28. In which country would you find Cardiff?
29. What would someone use to take your temperature?

30. How many times a year does the Queen celebrate her birthday?
31. Which big ship sunk when it hit an iceberg?
32. Tim Berners Lee created what that we use every day?
33. Bees make which sweet food?
34. What is the name of the person who runs a school?
35. What kind of an animal is Timmy in Timmy Time?
36. What is 10% of 200?
37. In a leap year, how many days are there in February?
38. Where was Paddington Bear from?
39. What kind of transport would you find at King's Cross Station?
40. What separates England from France?
41. If you were posting something, what would you stick on the front that has the Queen's head on it?
42. What is missing from this list: North, south, east and what?
43. What kind of animal has humps on its back?
44. What small official book would you need if you were going to leave the country?

45. What is the closest planet to the sun?
46. Forky was a character introduced to us in which film?
47. Sand is one of the things you need to make glass. True or false?
48. The Armada ships came from which country to invade England in 1588?
49. Who is England's current football captain?
50. If you had to write 20% as a fraction, what would you write?

Quiz 29: One Year Anniversary Quiz

ENTERTAINMENT

1. The 1979 movie Quadrophenia is loosely based on which band's album with the same name?
2. Name the Seventies TV show from this theme: "Here's the story, of a lovely lady, who was bringing up three very lovely girls. All of them had hair of gold, like their mother, the youngest one in curls."
3. What was the name of the 1985 movie starring Molly Ringwald and Emilio Estevez, The _____ Club?
4. Which female singer released the hits Wuthering Heights, Babooshka and Running Up That Hill?
5. Which Nineties TV show launched the careers of Mila Kunis and Ashton Kutcher: That _____ Show: '70s, '80s or '90s?
6. Who played The Riddler in the 1995 Batman Forever movie?
7. What was the name of the duo behind Macarena?

8. What was the spin-off to Buffy The Vampire Slayer called?
9. Alec Baldwin, Harrison Ford, Ben Affleck and Chris Pine on the big screen and John Krasinski on the small screen have all played which Tom Clancy-created character?
10. Zoom In was an EP released in March 2021 by which former Beatle?

IN WHICH COUNTRY WOULD YOU FIND......

1. Machu Picchu, Lima:
2. Mount Fuji, Tokyo:
3. Giza Necropolis, Cairo:
4. Rocky Mountains, Ottawa:
5. Narikala Fortress, Tbilisi:
6. Megalithic Temples, Valetta:
7. Moeraki Boulders, Wellington:
8. Ancient City of Petra, Amman:
9. Ha Long Bay, Hanoi:
10. Timbuktu, Bamako:

CONNECTIONS ROUND

1. What word beginning with B is a glass object used to hold fluids and chemicals in a laboratory?
2. In the musical Grease, who was the leader of the Pink Ladies?
3. Which fruit and nut salad is named after a hotel in New York?
4. What is the name of the skunk cartoon character from the Looney Tunes?
5. What transportation device also shares its name with the German happy hardcore band behind the Logical song?
6. Complete the name of the newspaper/movie character? The Secret Life Of ______ Mitty?
7. A tadpole takes about 14 weeks to become which amphibian?
8. In the nursery rhymes, what little things went to the market and had roast beef?
9. Complete the marketing slogan: Peperami, it's a bit of an...?
10. What links them?

GEBERAL KNOWLEDGE

1. What is the name of the ship which blocked the Suez Canal in 2021: Ever Green, Ever Given or Ever Broken?
2. The world's largest painting (1,600 sq. m) sold at auction for how much: £4.5 million, £45 million or £450 million?
3. Gamophobia is a fear of what: X-Rays, commitment or showers?
4. Who was manager the last time the England men's football team made it to a World Cup semi-final?
5. What is the third letter of the Greek alphabet?
6. Which of these three rivers is the longest: Mississippi, Amazon or Congo?
7. George V was reigning monarch for both World Wars One and Two. True or false?
8. What does the G stand for in GIF?
9. Pedagogy deals with which group, children or adults?
10. What does 0 degrees Celsius equal in Fahrenheit?
11. 1,760 yards equals how many miles?

12. Before joining the euro, which country had the Mark currency?
13. Which Welsh actor recently revealed he has handed back his OBE?
14. Footballer Lionel Messi has broken whose long-standing goalscoring record?
15. Name the song: "When you walk through a storm, hold your head up high, and don't be afraid of the dark."
16. According to legend, what was the shape of King Arthur's table?
17. What is the name of the medication that can be found in tonic water?
18. Who created the Mr Men/Little Miss book series?
19. J M Barrie famously gave the rights of Peter Pan to which hospital?
20. Who invented vulcanized rubber?

Quiz 30

TV AND FILM

1. Captain Mainwaring, Sergeant Wilson and Private Pike were characters in which TV show?
2. In which movie would you find The Truffle Shuffle?
3. Complete the name of the long-running US/UK TV show: Whose Line Is It...?
4. Who played James Bond in A View To Kill?
5. What was Del Boy and Rodney's uncle called in Only Fools And Horses?
6. Who played Beetlejuice in the 1988 film?
7. Kenneth Wolstenholme, Jimmy Hill, Des Lynam and Gary Lineker have all presented which sports show?
8. Which superhero has been played by Andrew Garfield, Tobey Maguire and Tom Holland?
9. In which TV series and one-off film did Jack Whitehall play teacher Alfie Wickers?
10. Which former Friends actress was one of the "Horrible Bosses"?

GEOGRAPHY

1. Altostratus, Stratocumulus, Cumulonimbus and Nimbostratus are all types of what?
2. Which sea does the Volga river flow into?
3. Which of the following airports are closest to Central London: London Heathrow, London Gatwick or London City?
4. In map terms, what does the O stand for in O.S Map?
5. What is the second-highest mountain in the world?
6. Which country does Gibraltar share a border with?
7. Are the Faroe Islands closer to Scotland or Denmark?
8. On which island would you find the river Medina?
9. Which river flows through or past Gloucester, Tewkesbury, Worcester and Shrewsbury?
10. Which country is completely landlocked by South Africa?

CONNECTIONS ROUND

1. Sherlock Holmes lived at 221B where?
2. Tucker Jenkins, Zammo, Pogo and Gripper were characters in which children's TV series?
3. What is the name for a statue, building or other structure erected to commemorate a notable person or event?
4. What was the name of the bear from Peru?
5. What shape is described as having a rounded and slightly elongated outline or shape like an egg?
6. A building devoted to the worship of god or gods are known as what?
7. What is NatWest, Lloyds and Santander types of?
8. Who makes the Astra and Corsa cars?
9. Which battle marked the end of the Napoleonic wars?
10. What links them all?

GEBERAL KNOWLEDGE

1. What stage name does Robert Van Winkle go by?
2. Winston Churchill was Prime Minister twice – who was premier in between his terms?
3. Which of these cities has the smallest population: City of London, Wells or St Davids?
4. Carlo Acutis is one step away from becoming the first millennial what?
5. Gazpacho soup is served hot or cold?
6. The Festival of Speed incorporating the famous hill climb is held where each year?
7. Which Beatle is Liverpool's airport named after?
8. A Promised Land is a memoir by whom?
9. Which motorway links Glasgow and Edinburgh?
10. In a standard game of Sudoku, how much would all the numbers total up to?
11. Mikhail Gorbachev announced his resignation as President on Christmas Day in 1991 from what former Empire?
12. What does the R stand for in the acronym RSPB?

13. If you are born on Christmas Day, what star sign what would you be?
14. How many points is the letter Q worth in Scrabble?
15. What does MMXXI represent in Roman numerals?
16. Which singer was born Jon Francis Bongiovi Jnr?
17. Which cartoon characters' catchphrase was "suffering succotash"?
18. Which country did Brazil declare independence from in 1822?
19. What product was the first UK TV commercial advertising in 1955?
20. Carrier, Cruiser and Submarine were some of the names of pieces in which board game?

Specialist Rounds

Ready for more? Here are plenty of questions to put your specialist knowledge to the test.

Superheroes

1. What does MCU stand for?
2. Which character has had the most screen time in the MCU films?
3. Apart from the four Avengers films, what is the highest-grossing MCU movie?
4. Who played Bruce Banner in the first Hulk movie in the MCU?
5. Natasha Romanoff/Black Widow first appeared in which MCU film?
6. How many infinity stones were there?

7. Which movie did Thanos first appear in?
8. What was the name of the Collector's dog in Guardians Of The Galaxy?
9. What does SHIELD actually stand for?
10. What was the name of the Super Soldier Project that created Captain America?
11. After the Battle of New York in Avengers, what did the characters go and eat?
12. What was Tony Stark's father called?
13. In the post-credits scene in the first Iron Man, who tells Tony he is not the only superhero in the world?
14. Terrence Howard played which role in the first Iron Man?
15. Which iconic actor took on the role of director for the first Thor film?
16. What was Dr Erik's surname, the man who helped harness the power of the Tesseract?
17. Where does Dr Abraham Erskine live?
18. The Super Soldier Serum fell under which project name?
19. Who directed The Avengers in 2012?

20. What is the name of Tony Stark's original AI?
21. Who played Jane Foster?
22. Who is inside the super computer that Captain America and Natasha activate in the super bunker in The Winter Soldier?
23. Bucky Barnes becomes known by which other name?
24. What is Star-Lord's other name?
25. Zoe Saldana played which character in the MCU?
26. Who was the voice of Groot?
27. What was thc namc of Stark's global defense programme he was trying to create?
28. What is the name of the other twin to Wanda Maximoff?
29. Who played Hank Pym?
30. Wanda, Hawkeye, Ant-Man and Sam Wilson join which side in civil war?
31. Who does Tony recruit from Brooklyn to join his side?
32. Who played Doctor Strange?
33. What is the name of Gamora's estranged sister?

34. The Vulture is the villain in which MCU film?
35. Ned is which superhero's best friend?
36. A recording of which MCU character causes Hulk to turn back to Bruce Banner in Ragnarok?
37. Who is Thor and Loki's father?
38. King T'Challa was the ruler of which kingdom?
39. Who is the first to warn that Thanos is coming?
40. Which of the infinity stones does Doctor Strange protect?
41. Who do the Guardians Of The Galaxy rescue in their ship in Infinity War?
42. Who is the Soul Stone's keeper?
43. And who does Thanos send to their death to get the Soul Stone?
44. How many ways does Doctor Strange see where the Avengers can win?
45. Which of the following survive the snap: Rhodes, Nick Fury, Maria Hill, Spider-Man, Groot or Doctor Strange?
46. Who plays the Wasp?
47. What is the name of the race of shapeshifting aliens

in Captain Marvel?

48. Who sacrifices themselves to gain the Soul Stone, when the Avengers go back in time in End Game?
49. Which of the Avengers performs the first snap to bring everyone back?
50. And who finally utters the immortal line, "Avengers Assemble"?
51. Not including animated films or Joker, how many actors have played Batman?
52. Who played the Green Lantern in the 2011 film?
53. Who played Lex Luthor in Batman V Superman: Dawn Of Justice?
54. Deadshot, Harley Quinn, Killer Croc among others make up which Task Force in Suicide Squad?
55. Who played Superman in the first feature film based on any DC Comic book character?
56. Who played Vicki Vale in Tim Burton's Batman?
57. Since 2017 who has played Wonder Woman?
58. Which DC Film also shares its name with a popular app that allows you to find a song that is playing?
59. Name the DC Film from these actors: Tommy Lee Jones, Jim Carrey and Nicole Kidman.

60. Since 1992, which film studio has been responsible for releasing the DC Films?
61. What is Wonder Woman's alter ego?
62. Who will play Black Adam in the upcoming film of the same name?
63. What is the alter ego of The Penguin?
64. In what year did Catwoman make her first appearance in DC Comics?
65. Who portrayed Harley Quinn in the early 2000s TV show Birds Of Prey?
66. What is the name of Dr Victor Fries' wife?
67. At what theatre did Thomas and Martha Wayne meet their demise?
68. George Perez drew comics for which superhero starting in 1987?
69. Which artist and writing duo created Batman?
70. Who are the adoptive family of Supergirl?
71. What is the name of Superman's superhero dog?
72. Harley Quinn kept what animals as pets?
73. Who voices Batman in the video game Batman Arkham Asylum?

74. In Batman Forever, what does Two-Face use in order to make decisions?
75. Who portrayed Clark Kent in the 2001 TV show Smallville?
76. Who is the original alter-ego to Black Canary?
77. Who is faster, The Flash or Superman?
78. What government organisation does Amanda Waller run?
79. Taskforce X is a codename for which group of anti-heroes?
80. Barbara Gordon was paralysed by which DC villain?
81. Doctor Manhattan is a superhero in which comic book series?
82. The Joker's Daughter is the daughter of which villain?
83. Who portrayed the Green Arrow in the TV show Arrow?
84. Eddie Nash was an alias for which DC character?
85. What was the name of the pit belonging to Ra's al Ghul?
86. What is the only weakness of Superman?

87. Black Manta is the villain to which superhero?
88. What is the Batman named on Earth 22?
89. Damian Wayne is the son of Bruce Wayne and whom?
90. Martian Manhunter was an original member of which superhero group?
91. Who portrays Supergirl in the TV show of the same name?
92. Who played the first on-screen Superman?
93. Captain Marvel is also known by what name?
94. What superhero was struck by lightning in order to gain his powers?
95. Titan is the name of a chemical compound from which videogame?
96. Dr Pamela Isley is better known by what name?
97. Commissioner Gordon was portrayed by whom in the Dark Knight trilogy?
98. What was Dick Greyson's job before taking on the mantle as Robin?
99. Jason Todd is which anti-hero?
100. What was the name of Batman's butler?

Harry Potter

1. What was the first line in the first film?
2. What colour sock is Dobby given that frees him?
3. Mrs Weasley shouts, “Not my daughter you (rude word),” to whom?
4. How many girlfriends does Harry have?
5. Who does Harry rescue from the Chamber Of Secrets?
6. What was the name of the secretive club that Harry leads?
7. Who kills the snake Nagini?
8. How many Horcruxes were there?
9. Who played Professor Slughorn?
10. What was Hermione’s Patronus?
11. What did Ron use to try to contact Harry at Privet Drive?
12. What name does Harry give to the conductor of the Knight Bus?
13. Who helped Harry Ron and Hermione find the

North Tower for their first divination class?

14. Who did Harry and Ron have to help with their potion preparation?
15. Whose pet rabbit was killed by a fox?
16. Who is the new Captain and Seeker of Hufflepuff Quidditch team?
17. And who else are we introduced for the first time ahead of the films as Ravenclaws' Seeker?
18. Who wrote down the whole week's passwords for Gryffindor Tower that allowed Sirius Black to break in?
19. What did Gryffindor finally manage to achieve at the third time of asking with Harry on the team?
20. Which subject did Hermione drop at the end of the year as she couldn't stand using the Time-Turner again?
21. Who wrote to the Dursleys to invite Harry to the Quidditch World Cup?
22. What did the Weasley twins give to Dudley to make his tongue swell?
23. "A thousand years or more ago, when I was newly sewn, there lived four wizards of renown, whose names are still well known." Who sung those words?

24. Who told Hermione that there are house elves living at Hogwarts?
25. Arthur Weasley was written about in the daily prophet, but what did they put his name down as?
26. What does SPEW stand for?
27. What was the name of the Head of The Department of Magical Games and Sports?
28. Who interrupted Harry's interview with Rita Skeeter?
29. Who checked over the four Triwizard champions' wands before the tournament?
30. Krum's wand was revealed to be created by whom?
31. What kind of animal was Bungy, that had learned to water ski according to the end of the news?
32. Dudley had recently become a junior champion at what?
33. What were the words in the Howler that Aunt Petunia received?
34. Dumbledore says he doesn't care what they do as long as the don't take him off what?
35. Molly Weasley and whom are cousins by marriage?
36. After being cleared of all charges, what did Harry do

with his money bag on the way out of the Ministry?

37. What was Ron made before Hogwarts started its first term?
38. Who struggled to destroy the Boggart in the study and was saved by Lupin?
39. What was the nickname given to Cornelius Fudge in the Quibbler?
40. "I'll be her friend as long as I don't have to borrow that cardigan." Who was Parvati talking about?
41. Which fellow student did the three hear nearby along with Tonks' dad and two goblins?
42. Whose portrait did Hermione take from Grimmauld Place?
43. Who did Harry keep staring at on the Marauder's Map?
44. What was written on Kendra Dumbledore's tombstone?
45. What name did Ron give the snatchers to escape them?
46. So he can sneak up on people, sometimes he gets bored of running at them flapping his arms and shrieking. Whose joke about death was this?

47. What kind of horn helped blow Xenophilius' house apart?
48. What was the name of the underground radio that they needed a password for to listen to?
49. 'Royal' was the radio codename for which wizard?
50. And who did they refer to as the chief death eater?

Disney

1. What Time Is It? is a song featured in which musical?
2. Which Disney channel star made a cameo in HSM2?
3. Wizards of Waverly Place featured which actress/ singer?
4. Which Disney Channel movie featured twins as witches?
5. DuckTales is the series which focuses on which character's family?

6. Which actor most recently voiced Scrooge McDuck?
7. Which actor played the Beast in the live action film?
8. Bop To The Top, Stick To The Status Quo and Getcha Head In The Game are all songs in which Disney musical?
9. Which actress plays both identical twin daughters in the film The Parent Trap?
10. What character can build a snowman?
11. Which actress voices Princess Anna?
12. Which Disney film features the character Mushu?
13. What is the name of the horse Merida rides?
14. What is the name of Woody's TV show in Toy Story?
15. What year did the first Disneyland open?
16. What is the name of Iron Man's AI?
17. What is Captain America's alter ego?
18. The Mandalorian is a TV show based in which film franchise?
19. What film features a nanny flying in on an umbrella?
20. Awesome Mixtape Vol 1 is featured in what film?
21. Who voices the character Groot?

22. Which comic book creator makes a cameo in most Marvel films?
23. Who was King Triton's composer?
24. What was Maurice's profession in Beauty And The Beast?
25. In which Disney film did Amy Adams portray a princess?
26. What was the name of the character Zac Efron played in High School Musical?
27. Lindsay Lohan drove which famous car in the 2006 remake?
28. What Dreams Are Made Of is a song featured in which Disney channel show turned movie?
29. Which movie takes a group of children to Neverland?
30. Flubber is a 1997 film starring which actor?
31. Matthew Broderick starred in the 1999 live action reboot of which character?
32. Who starred in the live action remake of Cinderella?
33. Which Broadway musical debuted on Disney+ this year?
34. What was the name of the greedy mouse in

Cinderella?

35. What is the name of the rat in Ratatouille?
36. Which actor plays Bert in Mary Poppins?
37. Fantasia starred which classic Disney character in the main role?
38. Who was Captain Hook's nemesis?
39. Who is Captain Hook's first mate?
40. Tinkerbell was the fairy to which classic character?
41. In which Disneyland theme park does the dragon reside below the castle?
42. Someday My Prince Will Come is a song featured in which film?
43. Which sorceress cursed aurora as a child?
44. Which actress portrays Maleficent in the live action films?
45. What does the evil queen entice Snow White to eat?
46. What is the name of the Pixar lamp?
47. What are the names of Bo Peep's sheep?
48. Who voiced Duke Kaboom in Toy Story 4?
49. What other name does Prospector Pete go by?

50. Life Is A Highway is a song featured in what Disney film?
51. Oswald was what kind of animal?
52. What was the first animation Disney released in 1937?
53. What was the first animation released by Pixar in 1995?
54. What are the colours that Flora, Fauna and Merryweather argue about for aurora in Sleeping Beauty?
55. What does Cruella De Vil want with 101 Dalmatians?
56. The song You're Welcome is featured in what film?
57. Brave was based in which country?
58. What character could see with all the colours of the wind?
59. Gaston was the villain in which film?
60. In which animated film is Prince Adam in?
61. What was the name of the cat in Cinderella?
62. What colours were Snow White's dress?
63. What kind of animation was used in early Disney films?

64. Kuzco was the emperor in which animated film?
65. Jafar was the villain in which film?
66. Timon and Pumbaa appear in which film?
67. In which year did Mickey Mouse make his debut on screen?
68. In what year did the song Let It Go grace the big screen?
69. Under The Sea is sung by what character?
70. What colour is the genie in Aladdin?
71. What is the name of Gaston's sidekick?
72. What is Lumiere?
73. What Disney princess does Emma Watson play?
74. In Frozen, what is the name of the trading post?
75. In Toy Story 4, which character makes a return after not appearing in the third movie?
76. Tim Allen voices which popular character?
77. What Easter egg is seen in every Pixar movie?
78. Which character is Boo seen holding in Monsters Inc?
79. Bibbidi-Bobbidi-Boo comes from which Disney princess musical?

80. Philip was the prince who had to rescue which princess?
81. Who was Ariel's father?
82. What was the name of the clock in Beauty And The Beast?
83. Who is the sixth Disney princess, although she plays more of a supporting role in the film?
84. Which Disney princess is the daughter of Chief Powhatan?
85. What is the name of the dragon that resolves to protect Mulan?
86. Tiana is working two jobs in order to raise money to turn a rundown sugar mill into what?
87. By what other name is Eugene Fitzherbert known in the movie Tangled?
88. What name is Experiment 626 renamed?
89. What kind of animal is Timon?
90. What is the name of the alien in Chicken Little?
91. What kind of animal is Bambi's friend Thumper?
92. Everybody Wants To Be A Cat comes from which Disney musical?

93. John Goodman provided the voice for which kind and caring village leader in The Emperor's New Groove?
94. What is the name of the restaurant in Lady And The Tramp?
95. Who does Esmeralda fall in love with in The Hunchback Of Notre Dame?
96. Where is Lilo & Stitch set?
97. In which city is the Princess And The Frog set?
98. "Just keep swimming" was said by what character?
99. Crush is a sea turtle from which film?
100. Al's Toy Barn is from which film?

Through The Decades

SIXTIES

1. What was the cost of a loaf of bread in the Sixties: 5p, 25p or 55p?
2. Which audio storage device was invented by Philips in 1962?
3. Which UK TV channel went on air for the first time in 1964?
4. And which UK TV channel was the first to have colour in 1967
5. What was the name of the British version of GI Joe, launched in 1966?
6. Which footwear, nicknamed DMs, gained in popularity at the start of Sixties?
7. Love Me Do was the Beatles' first number one in four countries, but what number did it reach in the UK? One, seven or 17?
8. Which British soap made its debut in 1960?
9. Which horse race was broadcast for the first time on 26 March 1960?

10. Which satirical magazine was launched for the first time in 1961?
11. What was the name of the doctor who called for huge cuts to the national railway system?
12. Which banknote was issued for the first time since the Second World War?
13. Which island country gained independence from the UK in 1964?
14. The Worboys Committee was set up to overhaul what in 1963?
15. The first what was pumped out of the North Sea in 1967?

SEVENTIES

1. Who was the Prime Minister of the UK at the start of the Seventies?
2. On 22 January 1970, what aircraft landed at Heathrow airport for the first time?
3. 19 September 1970 saw the first of which Somerset festival that is still running today?
4. Which university started broadcasting in 1971?
5. Complete the title of the Richard Adams novel released in 1972. Watership...?

6. Which British soap launched for the first time in 1972?
7. Mark Phillips got engaged to which Royal in May 1973?
8. What was the name of the text-based TV service launched by the BBC in 1974?
9. One of the worst London Underground Tube crashes occurred in 1975 at which station?
10. Anita Roddick opened the first retail branch of which shop in 1976?
11. Between 16 November and 1 June 1976, United Kingdom and Iceland were engaged in their third war against each other, but what was it called?
12. Featuring songs The Chain, Don't Stop and Go Your Own Way, what was the name of the Grammy award-winning album released by Fleetwood Mac in 1977?
13. BBC One and Two were forced off air due to a strike in 1978. True or false?
14. A naturist beach was established for the first time on which UK beach?
15. Who was the Prime Minister at the end of the Seventies?

EIGHTIES:

1. Which theme park was opened in the UK on 4 April 1980?
2. 1981 saw Mark David Chapman sentenced to 20 years to life in prison for killing whom?
3. What was the name of Henry VIII's flagship that sank in 1545 and raised from the Solent in October 1982?
4. What vehicle feature became compulsory for drivers and front-seat passengers in 1983?
5. The Brink's-Mat robbery saw 6,800 gold bars stolen from their vault at which UK airport?
6. Which Japanese car-maker signed a deal to build a car factory in Sunderland, the first time that foreign cars would be built in Britain?
7. Which communications company was privatised in 1984?
8. In 1985, who became the first post-war Prime Minister to be refused an honorary degree by Oxford University?
9. Mohamed Al-Fayed bought which department store in 1985?

10. Gary Lineker was the most expensive British footballer for 24 hours after which player moved from Liverpool to Juventus?
11. What was the name of the first driverless railway that was opened by the Queen in 1987?
12. What was the name of the BBC's second annual telethon, launched in 1988, following on from the 1980 launch of Children In Need?
13. Sandy Lyle became the first British winner of which golf tournament?
14. In 1989, were proceedings in the House of Lords or the House of Commons the first to be televised?
15. Which long-running BBC sci fi-drama came to an end after 26 years, later to be resurrected in the Noughties?

NINETIES

1. Who replaced Margaret Thatcher as Prime Minister in November 1990?
2. Which BBC national radio station starting broadcasting in 1990, the first new station for 23 years?
3. Which motorway opened in 1991, giving the West Midlands its first direct motorway link to London?

4. Which famous frontman died on 24 November 1991?
5. Part of which castle was damaged by fire on November 20 1992?
6. Which breakfast TV show launched in January 1993 and ran until 2010?
7. Nemesis, Europe's first inverted rollercoaster, opened where in the UK?
8. Which discount German supermarket opened its first 10 branches in the UK in 1994?
9. On 16 April 1995, Phone Day was a major change to geographic area codes, but which number was added after the zero?
10. Which boyband broke many hearts when they announced they would be splitting up on 13 February 1996?
11. Who became the most expensive footballer in the world at that time after a £15million transfer from Blackburn to Newcastle?
12. The new Labour government announced it would be banning what from sporting events in 1997?
13. After winning Eurovision in 1997, which UK city hosted the 1998 version?

14. Which new home movie format, first sold in the UK in June, sells just over 6,000 by the end of 1998?

15. Which TV presenter was tragically killed on her doorstep in 1999?

NOUGHTIES:

1. Who was the incumbent Prime Minister of the UK at the start of the millennium?

2. Which stadium was knocked down in October 2000 before a new stadium opened on the same site in 2007?

3. Which Tim Smit-conceived Cornwall tourist attraction opened in March 2001?

4. Which UK city hosted the 2002 Commonwealth Games?

5. In 2002, the mobile network BT Cellnet changed its name to what?

6. In 2003, EastEnders re-introduced which character after 14 years, and who was believed to be dead?

7. Which football club was bought in 2003 by Russian billionaire Roman Abramovich?

8. In 2004, The Hunting Act gained Royal Assent to ban the of hunting with what?

9. Which Royal couple got married on the 9 April 2005?
10. What was the name of the former supermarket chain that Morrisons took over?
11. Who greeted Tony Blair with the greeting "Yo Blair" at the G8 summit in Russia?
12. Who suffered a serious brain injury when the jet-powered car he was driving crashed whilst filming Top Gear?
13. What was banned from all enclosed public spaces in England on 1 July 2007?
14. Which High Street staple, famous for its pick and mix, announced their 807 stores would close by January 2009?
15. What TV signals began to be switched off in 2009 in the UK?

Children's TV

1. Who lived in a picnic basket?
2. What was the name of the children's character who wore a suit and a bowler hat?
3. In which TV show did the character Tobermory appear?
4. In which TV show did the character Officer Dibble appear?
5. In which TV show did the character Penfold appear?
6. In which TV show did the character Zelda appear?
7. In which TV show did the character Barney Gumble appear?
8. In which TV show did Pigs in Space appear?
9. In which TV show did the character Miss Kiki Frog appear?
10. In which TV show did the character The Iron Chicken appear?
11. In which TV show did the character Witiepoo appear?

12. In which TV show did a talking cat called Salem appear?
13. Who was the Saturday girl on Multi-Coloured Swap Shop?
14. What show was first presented by Emma Forbes and Andi Peters?
15. Moony and Sunshine were replaced by whom in Rainbow?
16. What sort of animal was Rag in Rag, Tag And Bobtail?
17. Who were Andy Pandy's two best friends?
18. Which family had a daily helper called Mrs Scrubbit?
19. What children's series was a predecessor to Monty Python?
20. What colour car had the registration FAB 1?
21. Who works his futuristic three-day week at Spacely Space Sprockets?
22. Who is the Captain of the Trumpton Fire Brigade?
23. Which Magpie presenter was the daughter of a star of the ITMA radio series?
24. What kind of creature was Gentle Ben?

25. Which US state was the setting for Flipper?
26. Who first presented ITV's Art Attack?
27. In which fictional village would you visit to meet Alf Thompson and Granny Dryden?
28. Who had a 1984 hit with the Fraggle Rock theme?
29. Which children's series is set in a youth club in the North East of England?
30. What colour hair grows on Edd the Duck's head?
31. What name was given to the masked character who threw custard pies around in TISWAS?
32. Which human originally appeared with Gordon the Gopher?
33. Which programme began, "Here is a house; here is a door; windows one, two, three, four..."?
34. Who provided the voices for the animals in Animal Magic?
35. Which children's TV show started with the words, "Here is a box, a musical box, wound up and ready to play"?
36. Which character was dressed as a jester in Rentaghost?
37. When Burgess Meredith was the special guest villain

in Batman, which character did he play?

38. Gerry Anderson's Stingray told about the adventures of Troy Tempest. Which organisation did Troy Tempest work for?

39. If Dill was a dog, what type of animal was Parsley?

40. Who was the artist on the TV series Vision On?

41. Who was the companion of Crystal Tipps?

42. Danger Island, The Micro Ventures, The Arabian Knights and The Three Musketeers were short segments in which classic children's TV programme?

43. Brinsley Forde, who went on to become the lead singer of Aswad, starred in which children's TV series of the 1970s?

44. In the cartoon series Danger Mouse, who provided the voice of Penfold?

45. Who created and wrote the TV series Maid Marian And Her Merry Men?

46. When Mr Benn was looking for an adventure, what type of shop did he visit?

47. In Worzel Gummidge, who played the character of Aunty Sally?

48. In the TV show The Flumps, how many Flumps were there?

49. What cartoon series featured a character called Little My?

50. The cartoon series Dogtanian And The Three Muskehounds was based on a book by which author?

Musicals

1. Which composer wrote Godspell, Pippin and Wicked?

2. American Idiot was a musical based on which band?

3. Which musical comedy features both puppets and humans live on stage together and is loosely based on a Sesame Street parody?

4. Which musical saw the performers on roller-skates?

5. Jersey Boys is based around which Sixties band?

6. Written by Lucy Moss and Toby Marlow, name the musical based around the wives of Henry VIII.

7. Ripped off from the movie Monty Python And The Holy Grail, name the musical.
8. Which Broadway musical was from the creators of South Park?
9. The Opening Night, The King Of Broadway and When You've Got It Flaunt It are musical numbers from which show?
10. Which musical was based around the fraternal twins Mickey and Eddie?
11. James Corden, Rebel Wilson and Idris Elba starred in which Andrew Lloyd Webber musical?
12. In which musical would you find the characters, Jenny Lind, Phillip Carlyle and Anne Wheeler?
13. Who starred as Sweeney Todd in the 2007 movie adaptation of the same name?
14. Name the five who were on the journey to see the Wizard Of Oz.
15. Come What May was an original song in which 2011 musical?
16. Pop, Six, Squish, UhUh, Cicero and Lipschitz are six women's way of explaining how they ended up in prison in which musical?

17. Which musical released in 1982 had the tag line, “The movie for tomorrow”?
18. Inspired by Romeo and Juliet, which musical saw the rivalry of the Jets vs the Sharks?
19. Michelle Pfeiffer and Maxwell Caulfield starred in which musical sequel?
20. Good Morning Baltimore is a song from which 2007 musical comedy?

Readers' Round

I asked my pub quiz fans for their own questions to appear in this book and they certainly didn't disappoint!

Alison Mason

1. What was the first toy to be advertised on television?

Stuart Obrien

2. In which sport did the actor Jason Statham represent his country at the 1990 Commonwealth Games?

Stuart Obrien

3. Which team has started top of the Premier League since it began?

Mike Torbitt

4. Who made their last appearance at Wembley on 28 June 1986?

Carol Elson

5. Who wrote the song Red Red Wine?

Clare Hodgson

6. What links these words: blanket, chain and cross?

Colin Colebrooke

7. Who is the mother of Huey, Louie and Dewey?

Hilary FitzGerald

8. What is a campanologist?

Dena Jordan

9. Name a sea that has no shores.

Roberts-Lewis

10. DCLXVI is what number in Roman numerals?

Geberal Normski

11. What was Boyzone's first UK number one?

Stuart Obrien

12. Which famous Billy Joel song does he flatly refuse to perform live?

Jude inman

13. What is a group of rabbits called?

Steven Alderson

14. The Louisiana Purchase of 1803 was an agreement between the United States and which other country?

Alex Singer

15. How many Games Maker volunteers were there at London 2012 (Olympics and Paralympics combined)?

Tony Curd

16. What do the BBC TV sitcom Dad's Army and the budget airline easyJet have in common?

Thomas Picton

17. Selangor, Perak and Melaka are states of which country?

Lin Hunt

18. There is officially only one lake in England's Lake District – what is it called?

Irene Pitt

19. What is the name of the highest waterfall above ground?

Irene Pitt

20. What gas is inserted into packets of crisps?

Alan Jackson

21. Which artist was the first to have consecutive releases enter the UK charts at number one?

Debbie King

22. What year was the last public execution by guillotine in France?

Rosemarie Espley

23. What is known as the Ship of the Fens?

Pat Brown

24. Selina Kyle is the real name of which comic book character?

Karen Lough

25. What is buried beneath the Wembley Stadium pitch?

Anne Marie Foot

26. How many bones are there in an adult human body?

Katharine Summerfield

27. Which is the only sport to have been invented for the Olympic Games?

Katharine Summerfield

28. Name the only three English counties where Stilton cheese is allowed to be made.

Michelle Snowden

29. What is a group of flamingos called?

Cathy Nute

30. How many permanent teeth does a dog have?

Cathy Nute

31. What is the name of the smallest planet in our solar system?

Alison Mason

32. Who directed, narrated and starred in the movie Matilda?

Carol Elson

33. How many hearts does an octopus have?

Christine Shayler

34. Who played Kid Curry in the TV series Alias Smith And Jones?

Victoria Bastiman and Nathan Seth

35. What is the Greek name for the capital of Cyprus?

Nathan Seth

36. What is the common name for the Mexican walking fish?

Jean C Coombs

37. What does a deltiologist study and collect?

Keith Turk

38. What vegetable has burpless varieties?

Samuel Ager

39. Which was the first film to have two actresses nominated for acting roles but playing the same character?

Ray Ellis

40. What is the name of the largest reservoir in the USA in terms of its capacity?

John & Christine Fountain

41. The fused collar bones in birds are called the Furcula, which is more commonly known as what?

Dulcie Reeve

42. Where would you find an example of a ziggurat, an ancient pyramidal temple structure?
    A) Peru B) Iraq C) Egypt

Julie Childs

43. What is the highest point on the south coast of England?

Maryann Mell

44. What is the only bird that can fly backwards?

Ian Johnson

45. Which musician links the following, Depeche Mode, Yazoo and Erasure?

Lynn Hoskins

46. What was the small pocket in a pair of jeans originally meant to hold?

Charlotte Gee

47. In the Harry Potter books, how many staircases are there at Hogwarts?

Simon Kimber

48. What is the 1923 FA Cup final famously known as?

Sue Johnson

49. Which author famously had cameos in the televised episodes of their books?

Paul Klein

50. Why did Niall James Horan, of One Direction fame, call their studio album from 2014 Four?

Simon Mackay

51. In the British army, the rank of sergeant (Sgt) is NOT used by the Household cavalry. What is their equivalent rank ?

Rudi Saunders-Green

52. Where were the 2016 summer Olympics held?

Lucy Morgan

53. Saying the name of what dried fruit used to encourage people to smile before a photo in the 1800s, before "cheese?"

Hazel Stainer

54. In 2004, what was discovered in Indonesia, on the island of Flores?

Marilyn Henshaw

55. Who would you be a fan of if you were a member of the Sons Of The Desert?

Cerys Macintosh

56. What is the only US state beginning with D?

Ian Alcock

57. Which motor race is always started by a Christmas tree?

Iain Richardson

58. What is the oldest international cricket fixture?

Graham Wheeler

59. What is the largest country in the world with only one time zone?

Kevin Nash

60. What year was Facebook founded?

Graham Wheeler

61. On a standard dart board, what is the lowest number you CAN'T score?

Jason Oxley

62. There were three kings of England called Edward before Edward I. True or false?

David Brooks-Smith

63. What is the mathematical name for a doughnut shape or rubber ring shape and is hollow inside?

Isabelle Chandler

64. Camilla Arfwedson played Sofia Walker in which American drama?

Raymond Barnett

65. What year was Winston Churchill born?

Isabelle Chandler

66. Which National Trust house did Anne Boleyn live in as a child?

Rob Millwood

67. Who made the cake on the Rolling Stones album Let It Bleed?

Quiz 1

ROUND 1: TV

1. June Brown
2. ER
3. Eddard Ned Stark
4. Scrubs
5. Thomas the Tank Engine
6. Pass
7. Arthur
8. Captain Pugwash
9. Michael Fish
10. Taxi

ROUND 2: SCIENCE

1. Jupiter
2. Four
3. Electron
4. Aluminium
5. Myopia
6. Tungsten
7. Density
8. Fool's Gold
9. Voice over Internet Protocol
10. Epsom Salts

ROUND 3: SPORT

1. 1986
2. Eiffel Tower
3. Spain
4. A Jack
5. Nine
6. Drag Reduction System
7. Baseball
8. 10 feet
9. UEFA Super Cup
10. Three

ROUND 4: PEOPLE

1. Elizabeth Taylor
2. Quasimodo
3. Larry King
4. Italian
5. Aaron
6. Margaret Thatcher
7. Elton John
8. Mark Twain
9. Shirley MacLaine
10. Princess Anne

ROUND 5: GEBERAL KNOWLEDGE

1. The Lion, The Witch And The Wardrobe
2. Chess
3. Stephen Schwartz
4. William Wordsworth
5. Electronic
6. Anne
7. iPod
8. One mile
9. One
10. 500

Quiz 2

ROUND 1: FILM

1. Steven Spielberg
2. Cal Hockley
3. Fight Club
4. Donald Trump
5. Stinky Pete
6. Edgar Wright
7. The Lego Movie
8. Volcano
9. Bob Too
10. John Travolta

ROUND 2: NATURE

1. Three
2. Female
3. Frogs
4. Lungs
5. 23
6. Mosquito
7. Zero Celsius
8. Wind speed
9. Mandible
10. Mammals

ROUND 3: ART AND LITERATURE

1. Boris Pasternak
2. Around The World In 80 Days
3. Margaret Mitchell
4. The National Gallery
5. Tom Clancy
6. Rip Van Winkle
7. Thumbelina
8. Woodstock
9. Wexford
10. Victor Hugo

ROUND 4: GEOGRAPHY

1. Istanbul
2. Mount Etna
3. Kentucky
4. Lagos
5. Melbourne
6. Swedish Krona
7. New York State
8. Mexican Peso
9. Adriatic Sea
10. Cook Strait

ROUND 5: GEBERAL KNOWLEDGE

1. Captain Hook
2. Christmas Tree
3. Virgo
4. Guyana
5. Four
6. Paper
7. Go
8. Mean
9. November
10. Lion

Quiz 3

ROUND 1: MUSIC

1. Elvis Presley
2. Railroad
3. Janet Jackson
4. Alanis Morissette
5. Susie
6. Ricky Martin
7. Three
8. Eric Clapton
9. A Rollercoaster
10. Baby

ROUND 2: FOOD AND DRINK

1. Eight
2. Maître D
3. Milky Way
4. On the ground
5. Italy
6. Whisky
7. Aniseed
8. Vegetables
9. Lentils
10. Rum

ROUND 3: HISTORY

1. 116
2. The Tower of London
3. Two
4. The Flying Fortress
5. The Mayflower
6. Nick Leeson
7. Eagle
8. Lord Lucan
9. Scotland
10. Louis XVI

ROUND 4: SCIENCE

1. Alkaline
2. Terabyte
3. Spain
4. Dynamo
5. Magenta
6. Sclera
7. Alexander Fleming
8. Oxygen
9. Colony
10. Blood pressure

ROUND 5: GEBERAL KNOWLEDGE

1. PlayerUnknown's Battlegrounds
2. Australia
3. Arthur
4. Polaroid
5. Dynamo
6. Backspace
7. Royal Flush
8. Olympic
9. Jim Davis
10. Glass

Quiz 4

ROUND 1: TV

1. Glee
2. Miss Marple
3. The Brittas Empire
4. Batman
5. Fun House
6. Happy Days
7. Steve Irwin
8. Wallace & Gromit
9. Al Murray
10. Wendy

ROUND 2: SPORT

1. Greece
2. Croquet
3. Assistant
4. Eldrick
5. 60 feet
6. 12 yards
7. Biathlon
8. 18
9. 10
10. Rugby Union

ROUND 3: PEOPLE

1. Anne Frank
2. Jane Fonda
3. Steve Jobs
4. Jack Ruby
5. Bob Dylan
6. Lembit Opik
7. Heston Blumenthal
8. Italy
9. Ted Kaczynski
10. Mark Zuckerberg

ROUND 4: PLACES

1. Lancashire
2. Australia
3. St. Moritz
4. Isles of Scilly
5. Sao Paulo
6. Cape Canaveral
7. Gobi
8. Singapore
9. Blue Mountain Peak
10. Agra

ROUND 5:
GEBERAL KNOWLEDGE

1. GTA 5
2. USA
3. Columbia
4. True
5. 8-track
6. FIFA
7. Blank
8. Dennis the Menace
9. Rollercoaster
10. Mediterranean Sea

Quiz 5

ROUND 1: FILM

1. Elliot
2. The Notebook
3. Tim Curry
4. Greased Lightning
5. Star Wars
6. Shark Tale
7. 1991
8. Willy Wonka
9. Gale
10. Jake and Elwood

ROUND 2: NATURE

1. Jill
2. Cow
3. A pride
4. Femur
5. Ear wax
6. Sleep
7. Bones
8. Population
9. Kit
10. Dog

ROUND 3: ART AND LITERATURE

1. J. R. R. Tolkien
2. Supper
3. The Book of Malachi
4. Anthony Gormley
5. H.G. Wells
6. 13
7. Moby Dick
8. Jane
9. Charles Dickens
10. Mario Puzo

ROUND 4: GEOGRAPHY

1. Tenerife
2. District of Columbia
3. Chennai
4. Africa
5. Lake Victoria
6. Madagascar
7. Sweden
8. Africa
9. Seven
10. Cyprus

ROUND 5: GEBERAL KNOWLEDGE

1. Pokémon Go
2. Andrew Lloyd Webber
3. Australia
4. Neptune
5. Freddie Mercury
6. Shut the door
7. Donkey Kong
8. Spurs
9. The Famous Five
10. Writing

Quiz 6

ROUND 1: MUSIC

1. The Shadows
2. ZZ Top
3. Andrew Ridgeley
4. The Verve
5. Etta James
6. Eight Days A Week
7. False
8. Meatloaf
9. Paul
10. Alison Moyet

ROUND 2: SCIENCE

1. The Leaf
2. The battery
3. Methane
4. Noses
5. Swedish
6. Mars
7. In the dark
8. Watts
9. Polyvinyl chloride
10. Bus

ROUND 3: FOOD AND DRINK

1. McDonald's
2. Sangria
3. Nando's
4. Bread
5. Marzipan
6. Coffee
7. Ice cream
8. Spinach
9. France
10. Thailand

ROUND 4: HISTORY

1. 815
2. Great Fire of London
3. Julius Caesar
4. Vesuvius
5. Bronze Age
6. Turkey
7. Bastille
8. Friendly
9. Romulus and Remus
10. Salvation Army

ROUND 5:
GEBERAL KNOWLEDGE

1. Watch Dogs
2. Nine
3. Daily Mail
4. Jekyll and Hyde
5. He was hanged
6. Bam Bam
7. 15
8. Bus
9. 360 degrees
10. Books

Quiz 7

ROUND 1: TV

1. Family Affairs
2. The Good Life
3. Gremlins
4. Happy Days
5. Lynda Carter
6. Cards
7. Designated Survivor
8. Nicholas Lyndhurst
9. The Big Breakfast
10. 52 Festive Road

ROUND 2: FOOD AND DRINK

1. Olive brine
2. Cadbury
3. Caramel
4. Pizza
5. Choux
6. Brandy
7. Bacon
8. USA
9. Pikelet
10. Heineken

ROUND 3: ART AND LITERATURE

1. Nelson Mandela
2. Spider
3. James Bond
4. Enid Blyton
5. C. S. Lewis
6. Music
7. Figaro
8. Rudyard Kippling
9. Heffalumps
10. Sistine Chapel

ROUND 4: PEOPLE

1. John Lennon
2. Joan of Arc
3. Blue Peter
4. Jessie J
5. Peter Kay
6. Darcey Bussell
7. Westwood
8. Lois Smith
9. Micahel Palin
10. Rob Brydon

ROUND 5:
GEBERAL KNOWLEDGE

1. Three
2. Vatican City
3. Henry
4. Alcohol
5. The Archers
6. Wagons/Wheels
7. Ice
8. 16
9. Throat
10. Cats

Quiz 8

ROUND 1: FILM

1. Die Hard
2. Dirty Dancing
3. Monty Python's Life of Brian
4. The Simpsons
5. Blue
6. Wall-E
7. Starship Troopers
8. 2½/33⅓
9. Mrs Robinson
10. Big

ROUND 2: SCIENCE

1. Poison
2. -40
3. Gravity
4. Boron
5. Ankle
6. Equator
7. Pangea
8. The Core
9. Venus
10. 118

ROUND 3: SPORT

1. Six
2. Caddie
3. Qatar
4. Blue
5. Golf
6. Paris Saint-Germain
7. American Football
8. Isle of Man
9. Phil Tufnell
10. Tennis

ROUND 4: GEOGRAPHY

1. California
2. Cuba
3. Beijing
4. Sargasso Sea
5. Dominican Republic
6. Canada
7. Belgrade
8. Tulip
9. Portugal
10. Dead Sea

ROUND 5:
GEBERAL KNOWLEDGE

11. Arnold Schwarzenegger
12. WhatsApp
13. 10,000
14. Andrex
15. Foghorn Leghorn
16. Charades
17. Linus
18. Uno
19. 13
20. Green

Quiz 9

ROUND 1: MUSIC

1. The Righteous Brothers
2. Elvis Costello
3. Talking Heads
4. N-Trance
5. Dusty Springfield
6. Fanilows
7. Wet Wet Wet
8. The Fray
9. Two
10. Europe

ROUND 2: NATURE

1. Chalk/limestone
2. False
3. Armadillo
4. Twice
5. Alligator
6. Cats
7. True
8. Gills
9. 32 km/h
10. True

ROUND 3: HISTORY

1. Catherine Howard
2. Moon landing
3. King John
4. England and Ireland
5. Britain
6. Tutankhamun
7. Enigma
8. Lady Jane Grey
9. Maastricht Treaty
10. Six

ROUND 4: PLACES

1. Oxfordshire
2. Won
3. Cymru
4. France
5. Stonehenge
6. 1997
7. Pisa
8. Karachi
9. Dubai
10. Bering Strait

ROUND 5: GEBERAL KNOWLEDGE

1. Teddy bear
2. Alcohol
3. Cards Against Humanity
4. Germany
5. 12
6. Pinocchio
7. Magna cum laude
8. Palindrome
9. Danny Boyle
10. Ikea

Quiz 10

ROUND 1: TV

1. 50th
2. The Likely Lads
3. Hollyoaks
4. David Tennant
5. Hollyoaks
6. Hill Street Blues
7. The Simpsons
8. Ross Geller
9. Air Crash Investigation
10. Creighton-Ward

ROUND 2: FOOD AND DRINK

1. Potato
2. Pringles
3. Beef
4. Yeast
5. Mozzarella
6. Earl Grey
7. Castlemaine
8. Stella Artois
9. Jimmy Carr
10. Yolk

ROUND 3: PEOPLE

1. Corfu
2. Abraham Lincoln
3. Rag 'n' Bone Man
4. Switzerland
5. Theodore Roosevelt
6. Spain
7. Albert Einstein
8. Michael Jackson
9. Mahatma Gandhi
10. Joseph Stalin

ROUND 4: SPORT

1. Curling
2. Four
3. Green
4. Hawkeye
5. 18
6. Dutch
7. Baseball
8. Boxing
9. Mulligan
10. Modern pentathlon

ROUND 5: GEBERAL KNOWLEDGE

1. The Winchester
2. Katrina & The Waves
3. Empty Orchestra
4. Four
5. Tycoon
6. Fortnite
7. Yellow
8. The Aft
9. £2
10. Giraffe

Quiz 11

ROUND 1: FILM

1. Richard Attenborough
2. You've Got Mail
3. Showgirls
4. Fast And The Furious
5. I've Got You Babe
6. South Park
7. 11
8. Moulin Rouge
9. Sheryl Crow
10. Spotless Mind

ROUND 2: SCIENCE

1. Magnetic resonance imaging
2. Hydrogen nitratc
3. Mercury
4. The Moon
5. Pollex
6. Silver
7. Noble gases
8. Refraction
9. Light
10. Atlantis

ROUND 3: ART AND LITERATURE

1. Peter Kay
2. Banksy
3. Rudyard Kipling
4. Words
5. Rapunzel
6. 36
7. Dawn French
8. Winston Churchill
9. Macbeth
10. Lewis Carroll

ROUND 4: GEOGRAPHY

1. Nevada
2. Lake Superior
3. Greece
4. The Shard
5. California and Nevada
6. Zambia
7. Caspian Sea
8. White
9. South China
10. Hong Kong

ROUND 5: GEBERAL KNOWLEDGE

1. Luigi
2. Plait
3. Abraham Lincoln
4. Cat's Eyes
5. 12
6. Five
7. Elton John
8. Henri Paul
9. Nellie the Elephant
10. Scalene

Quiz 12

ROUND 1: MUSIC

1. Five
2. Wizard
3. Tina Turner
4. Spirit
5. Santana
6. Christina Aguilera
7. Backstreet Boys
8. Barbados
9. Extended play
10. Wyclef Jean

ROUND 2: NATURE

1. Warm front
2. Jugular
3. Iron
4. Cob
5. Lactase
6. Mongooses
7. Kidneys
8. 12
9. Dog
10. Hydroponics

ROUND 3: SPORT

1. Canada
2. 200
3. Horse racing
4. Three
5. Norway
6. Tennis
7. Shanghai
8. Elephant
9. Table tennis
10. 10

ROUND 4: HISTORY

1. Winston Churchill
2. Catherine Parr
3. An execution
4. Hiroshima
5. 15th
6. Russian Empire
7. Operation Dynamo
8. 1949
9. Genghis Khan
10. Belgium

ROUND 5: GEBERAL KNOWLEDGE

1. Seven
2. Number
3. Hole In The Wall Gang
4. Quidditch
5. Bonn
6. Jaguar
7. Rumpelstiltskin
8. Ikea
9. 24
10. A

Quiz 13

ROUND 1: TV

1. Doctors
2. Only Fools And Horses
3. Grace Brothers
4. Eighties
5. Deal Or No Deal
6. Honah Lee
7. Bedrock
8. Snowball
9. Kelly Clarkson
10. The Incredible Hulk

ROUND 2: SCIENCE

1. Warning
2. Moons
3. Platinum
4. Force
5. Galileo
6. Graphite
7. Photosynthesis
8. Smelting
9. Life
10. Spam

ROUND 3: FOOD AND DRINK

1. Australia
2. Opal Fruit
3. Liquorice
4. Palm Tree
5. Carbon dioxide
6. Earl Grey
7. USA
8. Cyprus
9. Stomach
10. Cheese

ROUND 4: GEOGRAPHY

1. Statue of Liberty
2. New York City
3. Norfolk
4. Volcanoes
5. Canada
6. Russia
7. Michigan
8. Jersey
9. Afghanistan
10. The Andes

ROUND 5: GEBERAL KNOWLEDGE

1. Nine
2. Monday's child
3. London
4. Eskimos
5. F. Scott Fitzgerald
6. Channel Tunnel
7. Leonardo Da Vinci
8. George Washington
9. Cobalt
10. Brazil

Quiz 14

ROUND 1: FILM

1. Star Wars
2. Gone With The Wind
3. A Clockwork Orange
4. Ferris Bueller's Day Off
5. Chicago
6. Superman 3
7. Psycho
8. Moonraker
9. Anakin Skywalker
10. Shirley Temple

ROUND 2: NATURE

1. Bad breath
2. German Shepherd
3. Pancreas
4. Armpit
5. Ostrich
6. Haemoglobin
7. Forearm
8. Squid
9. Scar
10. Spine

ROUND 3: HISTORY

1. 1936
2. Catherine of Aragon
3. The Magna Carta
4. Overlord
5. Odin
6. Nine
7. Julius Caesar
8. Austria
9. 1941
10. Suffragettes

ROUND 4: PEOPLE

1. Monaco
2. Newfoundland
3. Italy
4. Alice Cooper
5. Italy
6. Stan Laurel
7. JFK
8. Colombian
9. Saatchi
10. Winston Churchill

ROUND 5: GEBERAL KNOWLEDGE

1. Futon
2. Bern
3. Saffron
4. 1995
5. Igneous
6. Aphrodite
7. Venus
8. Blue
9. Spain
10. Wasabi

Quiz 15

ROUND 1: MUSIC

1. Wilson Pickett
2. The Allman Brothers Band
3. News
4. Leonard Cohen
5. Neil Diamond
6. N Sync
7. Flo Rider
8. Scaramouche
9. The Rolling Stones
10. David Bowie

ROUND 2: SPORT

1. Nigel Benn
2. Lawn bowls
3. Churchill Downs
4. Ice hockey
5. Australian Open
6. Basketball
7. Rugby League
8. USA, Canada, Mexico
9. Four minutes
10. Germany

ROUND 3: ART AND LITERATURE

1. Jeremy Kyle
2. The Chronicles of Narnia
3. Viktor
4. Richard Adams
5. Paddington
6. Jules Verne
7. Amsterdam
8. John Constable
9. P. G. Wodehouse
10. Flamingos

ROUND 4: GEOGRAPHY

1. Kuala Lumpur
2. Vietnam
3. Cambridge
4. Yangtze
5. Birmingham
6. Red, white and blue
7. Italy
8. 12
9. Japan
10. USA

ROUND 5: GEBERAL KNOWLEDGE

1. Michael Crichton
2. Wright
3. Tanzania
4. Zeta
5. Sapphire
6. Dolly
7. Zeebrugge
8. Montague
9. Seven
10. Six

Quiz 16

ROUND 1: TV

1. Motel
2. Maplin
3. Life On Mars
4. Gladiators
5. Z Cars
6. Sarah Lancashire
7. Two Pints of Lager And A Packet of Crisps
8. Jerry Seinfeld
9. Will Young
10. Bad Girls

ROUND 2: SCIENCE

1. E=Mc2
2. Saturn
3. True
4. The Dog Star
5. Crystal
6. Phosphorus
7. The mantle
8. Carbon
9. Asteroid
10. Jet engine

ROUND 3: PEOPLE

1. Tim Peake
2. Falklands War
3. James I
4. Madonna
5. Mr T
6. Andrew Lloyd Webber
7. Australia
8. Tony Blair
9. Formula 1
10. Pee-wee Herman

ROUND 4: PLACES

1. Ibiza
2. Caracas
3. Bridge
4. Zimbabwe
5. Pyongyang
6. Peru
7. Lisbon
8. South Africa
9. Caribbean
10. Alaska

ROUND 5: GEBERAL KNOWLEDGE

1. Science and Nature
2. 180
3. Alabama
4. Her
5. Ethylene glycol
6. Fred Flintstone
7. Loving and giving
8. Reflex
9. Vietnam
10. Belgium

Quiz 17

ROUND 1: FILM

1. John Travolta
2. P.S. I Love You
3. Pulp Fiction
4. Green Lantern
5. Jason
6. Arnold Schwarzenegger
7. Dirty Dancing
8. Lego Movie
9. Daniel Radcliffe
10. Love Actually

ROUND 2: NATURE

1. Skin
2. 10
3. Knee cap
4. True
5. Neck
6. Thorax
7. 12
8. The Black Death/ Plague
9. Panda
10. Nose

ROUND 3: ART AND LITERATURE

1. His grandma
2. Sue Townsend
3. Lord of the Flies
4. The Bat
5. John le Carre
6. Alexandre Dumas
7. Upstage
8. Lew Wallace
9. The Scream
10. Gioachino Rossini

ROUND 4: HISTORY

1. White Star Line
2. Jamestown, Virginia
3. 1876
4. Poland
5. Winston Churchill
6. Egypt
7. 12
8. The Moon
9. 16th
10. Egypt

ROUND 5: GEBERAL KNOWLEDGE

1. Greek
2. Spencer
3. Mexico
4. South America
5. Estonia
6. Aliens
7. Perry
8. Gondola
9. Mediterranean Sea and Atlantic Ocean
10. Kathy Bates

Quiz 18

ROUND 1: MUSIC

1. Pink Floyd
2. 2Kiss
3. Hall & Oates
4. Curtis Stigers
5. Frank Sinatra
6. Miami Sound Machine
7. The Rat Pack
8. Revival
9. John Lennon
10. Salt-N-Pepa

ROUND 2: FOOD AND DRINK

1. Haribo
2. Italy
3. Sauerkraut
4. Mould
5. Japan
6. Calcium
7. Aubergine
8. Linguine
9. Biscuit
10. Typhoo

ROUND 3: SPORT

1. Aintree
2. Basketball
3. Pole vault
4. 50km walk
5. Nine
6. True
7. Luge
8. Five
9. Czech
10. Steve McLaren

ROUND 4: GEOGRAPHY

1. Pakistan
2. Seine
3. Pacific
4. Five
5. The Great Wall of China
6. Indian
7. Florida
8. Sweden
9. The Strait of Gibraltar
10. Romania

ROUND 5: GEBERAL KNOWLEDGE

1. Empty tomb
2. Train
3. Local
4. Red
5. Ghee
6. Falkland Islands
7. Europe
8. Sparrow
9. Bow and arrow
10. Far to go

Quiz 19

ROUND 1: TV

1. Take The High Road
2. Red Dwarf
3. Nine-Nine
4. Spice Girls
5. You Bet
6. The Inbetweeners
7. David Hasselhoff
8. Hawaii Five-O
9. Chief Clancy Wiggum
10. Dale Winton

ROUND 2: ART AND LITERATURE

1. One Hundred Acre Wood
2. The Stig
3. 24
4. Pablo Picasso
5. Bayeux Tapestry
6. Mary Ann Evans
7. Herbert George
8. Robert Ludlum
9. The Scarlet Pimpernel
10. D.H. Lawrence

ROUND 3: HISTORY

1. D-Day
2. Gordon Brown
3. HMS Victory
4. England and Norway
5. Frankfurt
6. 1910s
7. Scrolls
8. Roswell
9. England and France
10. Loch Ness Monster

ROUND 4: PLACES

1. Scafell Pike
2. Ankara
3. New York
4. Brazil
5. Danube
6. Buenos Aires
7. Netherlands
8. Germany
9. Iran
10. Mackenzie River

ROUND 5: GEBERAL KNOWLEDGE

1. Gazpacho
2. Daily Planet
3. Herman Melville
4. Liverpool
5. Fluke
6. Green
7. 1930s
8. Cherry
9. Singapore
10. Hard Black

Quiz 20

ROUND 1: FILM

1. Back To The Future
2. Pride And Prejudice
3. Little Shop Of Horrors
4. Jerry Maguire
5. Speed
6. Shrek
7. Mel Blanc
8. Superman
9. Reservoir Dogs
10. Bugsy Malone

ROUND 2: SCIENCE

1. Mercury
2. Backdraft
3. Ar
4. Wormhole
5. Alfred Nobel
6. Seven
7. Turin
8. Solar eclipse
9. Nitrogen
10. Celluloid

ROUND 3: FILM

1. Tennis
2. Argentina
3. Glazers
4. London 2012
5. 10
6. 12
7. Boris Becker
8. Mike Tindall
9. Norwich
10. South America

ROUND 4: PEOPLE

1. Canada
2. Josef Mengele
3. Programable computer
4. Harry Houdini
5. Kurt Cobain
6. Mark Zuckerberg
7. Julian Assange
8. Woody Allen
9. Argentina
10. Christopher Marlowe

ROUND 5: GEBERAL KNOWLEDGE

1. Red
2. Horsemen of the Apocalypse
3. Royal Mail Ship
4. Doc
5. Women
6. Full of woe
7. Russia
8. Velcro
9. Stockholm
10. Brazil

Quiz 21

ROUND 1: MUSIC

1. You Got It
2. Ramones
3. Eurythmics
4. East 17
5. Newcastle
6. Monday
7. Diana Ross
8. U2
9. The Sound Of Music
10. No Doubt

ROUND 2: NATURE

1. Australia
2. Vertigo
3. Tuberculosis
4. Face
5. Alzheimer's
6. Face lift
7. Cold
8. Spiders
9. Zero
10. DNA

ROUND 3: FOOD AND DRINK

1. Sausage
2. Bloody Mary
3. Polo
4. Mint
5. Apple
6. Bread
7. Vodka
8. Easter
9. Tequila
10. Toffee

ROUND 4: GEOGRAPHY

1. Stockholm
2. Four – Alabama, Alaska, Arizona, Arkansas
3. Wakefield
4. Aluminium
5. Stockholm
6. Wellington
7. The Rockies
8. China, Russia, Brazil
9. Alaska
10. Mallorca

ROUND 5: GEBERAL KNOWLEDGE

1. Pink
2. Pulitzer Prize
3. South Africa
4. Jamboree
5. Pagani
6. Generation
7. King Kong
8. Two
9. Israel
10. Jerk

Quiz 22

ROUND 1: TV

1. Goodnight Sweetheart
2. Your name
3. Eamon Andrews
4. Grange Hill
5. Thunderbirds
6. Ron Howard
7. Bungle
8. Extras
9. The Only way is Essex
10. Tipping Point

ROUND 2: SPORT

1. Six
2. Gymnastics
3. Darts
4. Hockey
5. Badminton
6. Cycling
7. Dublin
8. Rugby sevens
9. Sam Allardyce
10. Swimming

ROUND 3: HISTORY

1. Carpathia
2. Three
3. Normans
4. 1950s
5. Fukushima
6. Ronald Reagan
7. Treaty of Versailles
8. 1920s
9. Sophie Rhys-Jones
10. D-Day

ROUND 4: SCIENCE

1. Litmus paper
2. Jupiter
3. Eyesight
4. Operating system
5. U
6. Seven
7. Indigestion
8. Conjoined twins
9. Brass
10. Aspirin

ROUND 5: GEBERAL KNOWLEDGE

1. Portugal
2. Bugatti
3. Ukraine
4. Mardi Gras
5. Belize
6. Helicopter
7. Four
8. 17th
9. Angry Birds
10. Greece

Quiz 23

ROUND 1: FILM

1. Red and blue
2. Kylie Minogue
3. Rocky Horror Picture Show
4. Baseball
5. The Greatest Showman
6. No Time To Die
7. The Karate Kid
8. Sheffield
9. Chicago
10. Julia Roberts

ROUND 2: NATURE

1. Magpies
2. Pod
3. Lungs
4. Willow
5. Ravens
6. Mushrooms
7. Hippocratic Oath
8. Four
9. Phoenix
10. Four

ROUND 3: ART AND LITERATURE

1. The Old
2. Gretel
3. Louvre
4. Mary Norton
5. Anna Sewell
6. Beatrix Potter
7. Salman Rushdie
8. Richard III
9. Thomas Harris
10. J. D. Salinger

ROUND 4: PEOPLE

1. Anne Boleyn
2. Noddy Holder
3. Jamaica
4. Limp Bizkit
5. Ant & Dec
6. Judy Garland
7. Martin Luther King Jnr.
8. Jon Voight
9. Fleetwood Mac
10. Cary Grant

ROUND 5:
GEBERAL KNOWLEDGE

1. Avocado
2. Russia
3. Oven baked
4. Australia
5. General Lee
6. White
7. Peas
8. Seven
9. Pomegranate
10. St Lawrence Seaway

Quiz 24

ROUND 1: MUSIC

1. Simon & Garfunkel
2. Fleetwood Mac
3. The Pointer Sisters
4. Tears For Fears
5. The Beach Boys
6. Can't Fight The Moonlight
7. Paul Weller
8. Saturday
9. Swedish
10. Poker

ROUND 2: SCIENCE

1. Filament
2. Beagle 2
3. Chlorine
4. Sulphur dioxide
5. Lithium
6. AB Negative
7. Jupiter
8. False
9. Ozone
10. Four

ROUND 3: FOOD AND DRINK

1. Ice cream
2. Pot Noodle
3. Cherries
4. USA
5. Unsweetened
6. Haggis
7. Martini
8. Ham
9. An oven
10. Earl Grey

ROUND 4: GEOGRAPHY

1. Russia
2. Ickenham
3. Batman
4. Mediterranean
5. Texas
6. 11
7. Times Square
8. Five
9. The Rhine
10. Antarctica

ROUND 5: GEBERAL KNOWLEDGE

1. Java
2. 70
3. Jamaica
4. The Alps
5. 19
6. 13
7. Pakistan
8. Spain
9. Ottoman Empire
10. Cliff Richard

Quiz 25

ROUND 1: TV

1. Tardis
2. Tony and Gary
3. The Big Bang Theory
4. Gordon Burns
5. The Price is Right
6. Friends
7. Beverley Hills 90210
8. John Cleese
9. Naked Attraction
10. The Bodyguard

ROUND 2: NATURE

1. Panda
2. Bird
3. Diaphragm
4. Emperor
5. Fish
6. Tongue
7. Cholesterol
8. Chimpanzee
9. Groundhog
10. Kidneys

ROUND 3: ART AND LITERATURE

1. Dan Brown
2. Michelangelo
3. Pablo Picasso
4. Stephen Fry
5. Mark Twain
6. Chronicles of Narnia
7. Cain
8. Kenneth Grahame
9. Lend me your ears
10. Night Watch

ROUND 4: PLACES

1. Lesotho
2. Zambia and Zimbabwe
3. Las Vegas
4. Brazil
5. Reykjavik
6. Vatican City
7. Barbados
8. Spain
9. The Rhine
10. Indonesia

ROUND 5: GEBERAL KNOWLEDGE

1. Blackcurrant
2. 12
3. Poland
4. China
5. Pecorino
6. Palestine
7. Lamborghini
8. North
9. China
10. Rhode Island

Quiz 26 – Children's Quiz 1

1. London
2. TikTok
3. Dab
4. How To Train Your Dragon
5. Origami
6. Great Fire of London
7. US President
8. Maggie
9. Three
10. Basketball
11. The sun/light
12. 366
13. Helium
14. Scoop
15. Plumber
16. Washing machine
17. Lifeguard
18. Gru
19. Blackcurrant
20. 100
21. Noo-noo
22. Five
23. 1p

24. Hogwarts
25. Humpty Dumpty
26. Dinosaur
27. Tooth Fairy
28. Bob the Builder
29. 360 degrees
30. Apple
31. McDonald's
32. Two
33. Jigsaw
34. Where's Wally
35. Cow
36. Wrist
37. Boat
38. Berlin
39. Pudsey
40. Daleks
41. Teddy bear
42. Blue
43. Egypt
44. Downing Street
45. England, Scotland, Wales, Northern Ireland
46. Aunty
47. 26
48. GCSE
49. Hi Dr Nick
50. Ron and Hermione

Quiz 27 – Children's Quiz 2

1. Potato
2. Water
3. Easter
4. Laughing out loud
5. Three
6. Kitten
7. Bugs Bunny
8. Cars
9. Little Mix
10. ½
11. Swimming
12. Six
13. Mars
14. Girls Aloud
15. 100
16. Asia
17. 168
18. Three
19. The sun
20. World Wide Web
21. Prince Charles
22. Temperature
23. Oompa-Loompas
24. Muggle
25. Winnie the Pooh
26. The dish

27. Diamonds
28. The skull
29. Ice cubes
30. Hydrogen
31. Guy Fawkes
32. Blood
33. Food
34. True
35. 363
36. 10,000
37. Little Jack Horner
38. Mouse
39. Crown
40. Sing a Song a Sixpence
41. Seven: Red, orange, yellow, green, blue, indigo, violet
42. Mickey Mouse
43. Shrek
44. Ankle
45. Pokémon
46. North
47. Trains
48. Bob the Builder
49. Peter Parker
50. One

Quiz 28 – Children's Quiz 3

1. Four
2. 156
3. Peppa Pig
4. Giraffe
5. The Hulk
6. Six
7. Sleeping Beauty
8. Kid
9. Harry Potter
10. The equator
11. Peter Pan
12. Little Bo Peep
13. Basketball
14. True
15. Two
16. On a canal
17. Roblox
18. Robin Hood
19. Italy
20. Car
21. Marge Simpson
22. Three
23. Rugby
24. A farm
25. Batman
26. Tails

27. Ed Sheeran
28. Wales
29. Thermometer
30. Two
31. Titanic
32. Internet
33. Honey
34. Head teacher
35. A lamb/sheep
36. 20
37. 29
38. Peru
39. Trains
40. The English Channel
41. A stamp
42. West
43. Camel
44. Passport
45. Mercury
46. Toy Story 4
47. True
48. Spain
49. Harry Kane
50. 1/5

Quiz 29 – One Year Anniversary Quiz

ENTERTAINMENT

1. The Who
2. The Brady Bunch
3. Breakfast
4. Kate Bush
5. 70s
6. Jim Carrey
7. Los Del Rio
8. Angel
9. Jack Ryan
10. Ringo Starr

IN WHICH COUNTRY WOULD YOU FIND...

1. Peru
2. Japan
3. Egypt
4. Canada
5. Georgia
6. Malta
7. New Zealand
8. Jordan
9. Vietnam
10. Mali

CONNECTIONS ROUND

1. Beaker
2. Rizzo
3. Waldorf
4. Pepe Le Pew
5. Scooter
6. Walter
7. Frog
8. Piggy
9. Animal
10. Muppet characters

GEBERAL KNOWLEDGE

1. Ever Given
2. £45 million
3. Commitment
4. Gareth Southgate
5. Gamma
6. Amazon
7. False
8. Graphics
9. Children
10. 32
11. One
12. Germany
13. Michael Sheen
14. Pele
15. You'll Never Walk Alone
16. Round
17. Quinine
18. Roger Hargreaves
19. Great Ormond Street
20. Charles Goodyear

QUIZ 30

TV AND FILM:

1. Dad's Army
2. The Goonies
3. Anyway
4. Roger Moore
5. Uncle Albert
6. Michael Keaton
7. Match of the Day
8. Spiderman
9. Bad Education
10. Jennifer Aniston

GEOGRAPHY

1. Clouds
2. Caspian Sea
3. London City
4. Ordnance
5. K2
6. Spain
7. Scotland
8. Isle of Wight
9. River Severn
10. Lesotho

CONNECTIONS ROUND

1. Baker Street
2. Grange Hill
3. Monument
4. Paddington
5. Oval
6. Temple
7. Bank
8. Vauxhall
9. Waterloo
10. London Underground stations

GEBERAL KNOWLEDGE

1. Vanilla Ice
2. Clement Atlee
3. St David's
4. Saint
5. Cold
6. Goodwood
7. John Lennon
8. Barack Obama
9. M8
10. 405
11. USSR
12. Royal

13. Capricorn
14. 10
15. 2021
16. Jon Bon Jovi
17. Sylvester
18. Portugal
19. Toothpaste
20. Battleships

Specialist Answers

SUPERHEROES:

1. Marvel Cinematic Universe
2. Tony Stark/Iron Man
3. Black Panther
4. Edward Norton
5. Iron Man 2
6. Six
7. The Avengers
8. Cosmo the Spacedog
9. Strategic Homeland Intervention, Enforcement and Logistics Division
10. Project Rebirth
11. Shawarma
12. Howard
13. Nick Fury
14. James Rhodes
15. Kenneth Branagh
16. Selvig
17. Queens, but he was from Germany
18. Rebirth
19. Joss Whedon
20. Jarvis
21. Natalie Portman
22. Arnim Zola
23. The Winter Soldier
24. Peter Quill
25. Gamora
26. Vin Diesel
27. Ultron

28. Quicksilver/Pietro
29. Michael Douglas
30. Captain America
31. Spiderman/Peter Parker
32. Benedict Cumberbatch
33. Nebula
34. Spiderman Homecoming
35. Spiderman/Peter Parker
36. Black Widow/Natasha Romanoff
37. Odin
38. Wakanda
39. Bruce Banner
40. Time Stone
41. Thor
42. Red Skull
43. Gamora
44. One
45. Rhodes
46. Evangeline Lilly
47. Skrulls
48. Black Widow
49. Bruce Banner
50. Captain America
51. Six
52. Ryan Reynolds
53. Jesse Eisenberg
54. Task Force X
55. George Reeves
56. Kim Basinger
57. Gal Gadot
58. Shazam
59. Batman Forever
60. Warner
61. Diana Prince

62. Dwayne Johnson
63. Oswald Cobblepot
64. 1940
65. Mia Sara
66. Nora
67. Monarch Theatre
68. Wonder Woman
69. Bob Kane and Bill Finger
70. Fred and Edna Danvers
71. Krypto
72. Hyenas
73. Kevin Conroy
74. Coin
75. Tom Welling
76. Dinah Drake
77. The Flash
78. A.R.G.U.S
79. Suicide Squad
80. The Joker
81. Watchmen
82. Harvey Dent
83. Stephen Amell
84. The Riddler
85. Lazarus
86. Kryptonite
87. Aquaman
88. The Batman Who Laughs
89. Talia al Ghul
90. Justice League
91. Melissa Benoist
92. Kirk Alyn
93. Shazam
94. The Flash
95. Arkham Asylum
96. Poison Ivy

97. Gary Oldman
98. Acrobat
99. Red Hood
100. Alfred

HARRY POTTER

1. "I should have known you'd be here"
2. Grey
3. Bellatrix Lestrange
4. Two
5. Ginny
6. Dumbledores Army
7. Neville Longbottom
8. Seven
9. Jim Broadbent
10. Otter
11. Telephone
12. Neville Longbottom
13. Sir Cadogan
14. Draco Malfoy
15. Lavender Brown
16. Cedric Diggory
17. Cho Chang
18. Neville Longbottom
19. Win the Quidditch Cup
20. Muggle Studies
21. Molly Weasley
22. Ton Tongue Toffee
23. The Sorting Hat
24. Nearly Headless Nick
25. Arnold
26. Society for the Promotion of Elfish Welfare
27. Ludo Bagman
28. Dumbledore
29. Mr Ollivander

30. Gregorovitch
31. Bird/Budgie
32. Boxing
33. Remember my last Petunia
34. The Chocolate Frog Cards
35. Sirius Black
36. He emptied it into the pool in the atrium
37. A prefect
38. Mrs Weasley
39. Goblin Crusher
40. Dolores Umbridge
41. Dean Thomas
42. Phineas Nigellus
43. Ginny
44. Where your treasure is, there will your heart be also
45. Stan Shunpike
46. Rons
47. Erumpent
48. Potterwatch
49. Kingsley Shacklebolt
50. Voldemort

DISNEY

1. High School Musical 2
2. Miley Cyrus
3. Selena Gomez
4. Twitches
5. Donald Duck
6. David Tennant
7. Dan Stevens
8. High School Musical
9. Lindsay Lohan
10. Elsa
11. Kristen Bell

12. Mulan
13. Angus
14. Woody's Roundup
15. 1955
16. Jarvis
17. Steve Rogers
18. Star Wars
19. Mary Poppins
20. Guardians Of The Galaxy
21. Vin Diesel
22. Stan Lee
23. Sebastian
24. Inventor
25. Enchanted
26. Troy Bolton
27. Herbie
28. The Lizzie McGuire Movie
29. Peter Pan
30. Robin Williams
31. Inspector Gadget
32. Lily James
33. Hamilton
34. Gus
35. Remy
36. Dick Van Dyke
37. Mickey Mouse
38. Peter Pan
39. Mr. Smee
40. Peter Pan
41. Paris
42. Snow White And The Seven Dwarves
43. Maleficent
44. Angelina Jolie
45. Poison apple
46. Luxo

47. Billy, goat and gruff
48. Keanu Reeves
49. Stinky Pete
50. Cars
51. Rabbit
52. Snow White And The Seven Dwarves
53. Toy Story
54. Blue and pink
55. Their fur
56. Moana
57. Scotland
58. Pocahontas
59. Beauty And The Beast
60. Beauty and the beast
61. Lucifer
62. Blue and yellow
63. Celluloid animation
64. The Emperor's New Groove
65. Aladdin
66. The Lion King
67. 1928
68. 2013
69. Sebastian
70. Blue
71. LeFou
72. Candlestick
73. Belle
74. Wandering Oaken's Trading Post
75. Bo Peep
76. Buzz Lightyear
77. A113
78. Jessie the Yodelling Cowgirl
79. Cinderella
80. Aurora
81. King Triton
82. Cogsworth

83. Jasmine
84. Pocahontas
85. Mushu
86. A restaurant
87. Flynn
88. Stitch
89. Meercat
90. Kirby
91. Rabbit
92. Aristocats
93. Pacha
94. Tony's
95. Pheobus
96. Hawaii
97. New Orleans
98. Dory
99. Finding Nemo
100. Toy Story 2

THROUGH THE DECADES: SIXTIES

1. 5p
2. Compact Cassette
3. BBC Two
4. BBC Two
5. Action Man
6. Doc Martens
7. 17
8. Coronation Street
9. Grand National
10. Private Eye
11. Richard Beeching
12. £10
13. Malta
14. Road signs
15. Gas

SEVENTIES

1. Harold Wilson
2. Boeing 747
3. Glastonbury
4. Open University
5. Down
6. Emmerdale Farm
7. Princess Anne
8. Ceefax
9. Moorgate
10. The Body Shop
11. The Cod War
12. Rumours
13. True
14. Brighton
15. Margaret Thatcher

EIGHTIES:

1. Alton Towers
2. John Lennon
3. Mary Rose
4. Seatbelts
5. Heathrow
6. Nissan
7. BT
8. Margaret Thatcher
9. Harrods
10. Ian Rush
11. The Docklands Light Railway
12. Red Nose Day
13. US Masters
14. Commons
15. Doctor Who

NINETIES

1. John Major
2. Radio 5
3. M40
4. Freddie Mercury
5. Windsor Castle
6. GMTV
7. Alton Towers
8. Lidl
9. One
10. Take That
11. Alan Shearer
12. Tobacco advertising
13. Birmingham
14. DVDs
15. Jill Dando

NOUGHTIES:

1. Tony Blair
2. Wembley
3. The Eden Project
4. Manchester
5. O2
6. Den Watts
7. Chelsea
8. Dogs
9. Charles and Camilla
10. Safeway
11. George W Bush
12. Richard Hammond
13. Smoking
14. Woolworths
15. Analogue

CHILDREN'S TV

1. Andy Pandy
2. Mr Benn
3. The Wombles
4. Top Cat
5. Danger Mouse
6. Terrahawks
7. The Simpsons
8. The Muppets
9. Hector's House
10. The Clangers
11. H. R. Pufnstuf
12. Sabrina
13. Sarah Greene
14. Live and Kicking
15. George and Zippy
16. Hedgehog
17. Teddy and Looby Lou

18. The Woodentops
19. Do Not Adjust Your Set
20. Pink
21. George Jetson
22. Captain Flack
23. Jenny Hanley
24. A bear
25. Florida
26. Neil Buchanan
27. Greendale
28. The Fraggles
29. Byker Grove
30. Green
31. The Phantom Flan Flinger
32. Philip Schofield
33. Play School
34. Johnny Morris
35. Camberwick Green
36. Timothy Claypole
37. The Penguin
38. WASP (World Aquanaut Security Patrol)
39. A lion (on the TV show The Herbs)
40. Tony Hart
41. Alistair
42. The Banana Splits
43. Here Come The Double Deckers
44. Terry Scott
45. Tony Robinson
46. A fancy dress shop
47. Una Stubbs
48. Six (Grandpa Flump, Father Flump, Mother Flump, Posie, Perkin, Pootle)
49. The Moomins
50. Alexandre Dumas

MUSICALS

1. Stephen Schwartz
2. Green Day
3. Avenue Q
4. Starlight Express
5. The Four Seasons
6. Six
7. Spamalot
8. Book of Mormon
9. The Producers
10. Blood Brothers
11. Cats
12. The Greatest Showman
13. Johnny Depp
14. Dorothy, Scarecrow, Tin Man, Cowardly Lion and Toto
15. Moulin Rogue
16. Chicago
17. Annie
18. West Side Story
19. Grease 2
20. Hairspray

Readers' Answers

1. Mr Potato Head
2. Diving
3. Arsenal
4. Wham
5. Neil Diamond
6. They are all embroidery stitches
7. Della Duck, otherwise known as Dumbella Duck
8. A bellringer
9. The Sargasso Sea
10. 666
11. Words
12. We Didn't Start The Fire
13. A fluffle
14. France
15. 70,000
16. The closing credits for Dad's Army and the graphics on the easyJet aeroplanes are both in the same font (Cooper Black)
17. Malaysia
18. Bassenthwaite Lake
19. Angel Falls, Venezuela
20. Nitrogen
21. Slade in 1973 with Cum On Feel The Noise and Skweeze Me Pleeze Me
22. 1937
23. Ely Cathedral

24. Catwoman
25. A railway locomotive
26. 206
27. The modern pentathlon
28. Leicestershire, Nottinghamshire and Derbyshire
29. A flamboyance
30. 42
31. Mercury
32. Danny Devito
33. Three
34. Ben Murphy
35. Lefkosia
36. Axolotl
37. Postcards
38. Cucumber
39. Titanic (Kate Winslet and Gloria Stuart)
40. Lake Mead, Nevada (26.12 million acre-feet)
41. Wishbone
42. B) Iraq
43. Golden Cap
44. Hummingbird
45. Vince Clarke
46. A watch
47. 142
48. The White Horse Final
49. Colin Dexter in Inspector Morse
50. It was the band's fourth album
51. Corporal Of Horse (CoH)

52. Rio
53. Prunes
54. Skeletons of hobbit-sized humans
55. Laurel and Hardy
56. Delaware
57. Drag racing
58. USA v Canada, played in New York, September 1844
59. China
60. 2004
61. 23
62. True
63. A torus
64. MacGyver
65. 1874
66. Blickling Hall
67. Delia Smith

Charities and Support

Jay's Virtual Pub Quiz has worked with many charities but we wanted to highlight these four and encourage you to make your own donations and support.

NHS Charities Together is a collective experience representing, supporting and championing the work of the NHS's official charities. This was the first charity we worked with and it raised nearly £200,000 for them, which stands as one of their biggest fundraisers. As the quiz started after the NHS clap for carers, this was the perfect charity choice for a number of weeks. Donate at www.justgiving.com/originalvirtualpubquiz.

The Connection at St Martin's helps thousands of people every year to move away from, and stay off, the streets of London. This charity supported Jay during his time of need. Find out more at www.justgiving.com/virtualpubquizcstm.

The Diana Award is a living legacy to Princess Diana's belief that young people have the power to change the world for the better. Alex works there as Deputy CEO, and we supported their anti-bullying programme after Alex shared his own experience of bullying when he was younger. You can read more about the fundraising effort at www.justgiving.com/virtualpubquiz2.

Alzheimer's Research UK is the country's leading dementia

research charity, dedicated to causes, diagnosis, prevention, treatment and cure.We have helped this charity raise over £300,000, with one night alone hosted by Stephen Fry raising £200,000! As a result we went on to run a series of Friday takeovers with the likes of Jonathan Ross and Scarlett Moffat hosting. You can make a donation at www.justgiving.com/virtualpubquizaruk.

#JaysVirtualPubQuiz is live from 19:50 BST on Thursdays and Saturdays for a 20:15 quiz start time, and specialist pre-records are uploaded almost daily!

youtube.com/TheVirtualPubQuiz

facebook.com/JaysVirtualPubQuiz

twitter.com/TheVirtualPubQ1 @TheVirtualPubQ1

instagram.com/thevirtualpubquiz/ @TheVirtualPubQuiz

Website: jaysvirtualpubquiz.com

Support Jay by becoming a member:
www.patreon.com/thevirtualpubquiz

Get your merchandise at:
jays-virtual-pub-quiz.teemill.com and prezzybox.com/jay

Thank Yous

Firstly Sarah, you have been incredible this past 18 months, not only working for the NHS throughout the toughest time, but also in raising our incredible little munchkin into the talented, intelligent tiny terror we have today. Thank you for all of your support whilst this crazy journey continues.

To Alex, where on Earth would I be without you and your bits and pieces! But seriously, how you juggle your workload astounds me and how you remain positive in some of our most challenging times and keeping me from climbing the walls is a testament to you, and I'm glad throughout all of this I have a friend for life.

Bek, I told you this would be fun! Thank you so much for joining our team for being a fantastic friend and eating all of the sweets in the office on a Thursday night. You are amazing and your ideas and creativity are just amazing, and I'm honoured to call you my friend.

To my mum, quite simply thank you. It's been tough, but thanks for all the love, encouragement and support

To my friends, old friendships have been strengthened, new ones have been forged, some have left the circle, but to all of you, I appreciate you being there for me when I've needed a rant or to take my mind off things.

Zoe, Richie, Team News and The Prod Squad. No matter how I'm feeling, when one of you rings me on a Thursday morning to make sure I'm awake, your positivity never fails to lift me up and make me smile. Thanks for continuing to allow me to be a part of the show every week!

To the Geberal Nutjobs and all of the Patreons. Without your support, none of this would be possible. Our Patreon discord server is the most positive place on social media, and you guys never fail to raise a smile. Too many of you to name individually, but I thank you all for everything you have done.

To Hayley, Jen, Kitty, Lisa, Paige, Sian, Ben and Susan and not forgetting our good friend Cliff. Without you Quiz Jockey doesn't work, you guys give up your time twice a week and for that I am so grateful, thank you for the weird and wonderful Zoom calls after every quiz, and dare I say friends for life have been made. Also a massive thank you to Michael for allowing us to continuing to use Quiz Jockey, I'm eternally grateful for all of your support and advice.

To Hayley, the future looks bright because of your enthusiasm and passion for the crazy ideas I have. For the advice you have given me now at the time of writing and in advance of what's to come, thank you.

And finally to you, reading this, I never imagined having one book written in my life, let alone two. So thank you to you for having this in your hands.

Notes

Notes

Notes

Notes

Notes